CW00407149

£1-

KIDS' KITCHEN

BURGERS AND HOT DOGS

KIDS' KITCHEN

BURGERS AND HOT DOGS

DEVILISHLY DELICIOUS QUICK AND
EASY RECIPES FOR JUNIOR CHEFS

GINA STEER

APPLE

A Quintet Book

Published by The Apple Press
6 Blundell Street
London N7 9BH

Copyright © 1995 Quintet Publishing
Limited.
All rights reserved. No part of this
publication may be reproduced, stored in a
retrieval system or transmitted in any form
or by any means, electronic, mechanical,
photocopying, recording or otherwise,
without the permission of the copyright
holder.

ISBN 1-85076-627-4

This book was designed and produced by
Quintet Publishing Limited
6 Blundell Street
London N7 9BH

Creative Director: Richard Dewing
Designer: Ian Hunt
Project Editor: Anna Briffa
Editor: Emma Tolkien
Photographer: Andrew Sydenham
Home Economist: Gina Steer
Hand Model: Anna Callund

Typeset in Great Britain by
Central Southern Typesetters, Eastbourne
Manufactured in Singapore by
Eray Scan Pte Ltd
Printed in Singapore by
Star Standard Industries (Pte) Ltd

Acknowledgments
Special thanks to Spencer and Victoria
Dewing, Tom Lolobo, Gee Hyun Kim,
Nick Seruwagi, James and Lucy Stuart, and
to Bob McNiff of the Burlington Junior
School, Surrey, England.

Publisher's Note

Children should take great care when cooking. Certain techniques such as slicing and chopping or using the stove, oven or grill can be dangerous and extreme care must be exercised at all times. Adults should always supervise while children work in the kitchen.

As far as methods and techniques mentioned in this book are concerned, all statements, information and advice given here are believed to be true and accurate. However, the author, copyright holder, nor the publisher can accept any legal liability for errors or omissions.

Contents

BODENSEE
RED SOX

Introduction

Cooking is fun and the earlier you start the sooner you realize this. After all there are not many hobbies where you actually get to participate more fully than with cooking, and at the end you can eat whatever it is that you have prepared and cooked, and that has got to be good.

This book has been written with you, children, in mind. The recipes are designed to appeal to your tastes and appetites, and are simple to prepare and cook. There are easy-to-follow steps showing every stage to ensure a perfect result every time, with any steps that need adult supervision clearly marked.

It's never too soon to start learning about a good diet to provide a healthy lifestyle, good hygiene habits and the simple basics in food preparation and cooking. So, if this is your first attempt at cooking, start with the easy recipes that make use of convenience foods then, when you become more confident, move on to the slightly more involved recipes.

Do read the introduction pages before you begin to cook, which you are sure to find helpful, but most of all have fun and enjoy what you are doing.

HAPPY COOKING!

Before You Begin

Hygiene

- Good hygiene habits in the kitchen are of vital importance in order to avoid tummy upsets. Germs can easily be passed on and they grow well in dirty conditions or where it is warm and wet. Germs hate clean, dry, cold and bright places so it is important to make sure that the home is clean.
- Always wash your hands before beginning to cook or after going to the bathroom.
- Avoid touching your face or hair and if your hair is long, tie it back off your face.
- If you have a cut or sore on your hands, cover with a plaster before starting to cook.
- Keep pets out of the kitchen and wash your hands after touching them.
- Check that work surfaces, implements and cloths are clean before beginning to cook.
- Never prepare raw and cooked foods on the same chopping board or with the same implements without washing them in between use.
- Ensure that food is stored correctly. In the refrigerator, check the temperature is at 5°C and that juices from one food do not drip on to other foods.
- Wrap foods stored in the refrigerator correctly so that flavours and smells do not mix.
- Cool hot food first before storing in the refrigerator.
- If using frozen poultry, thaw thoroughly before cooking and ensure that all poultry is completely cooked before eating.
- Never refreeze frozen food that is partially thawed. Always thaw and cook it before refreezing it.
- Thaw frozen foods in the refrigerator rather than a warm room.
- Ensure food is rotated and that it is used by its "use by date".
- Avoid damaged or dented cans.
- Wash all fresh foods thoroughly before eating.
- Store chilled foods as quickly as possible in the refrigerator after purchase.
- Always use a clean spoon to taste your food when cooking.

Eat Well

It is important that the food we eat provides a good balanced diet. As with an engine, which needs the right balance of fuel, oil and water, so it is with us. It is by eating the correct foods that we ensure we grow and develop and stay healthy.

- The body needs plenty of liquid so it is important to drink plenty of water, semi-skimmed milk or juice. Try to avoid too many fizzy drinks.
- Eat plenty of pasta, cereals, rice, fresh fruit and vegetables and a smaller amount of lean meat, fish, eggs and cheese.
- Biscuits, cakes, fried foods and sweets should be avoided as much as possible and only eaten as treats.

Ready Steady

- First check with an adult that it is OK for you to use the kitchen and that someone will be around to help you when necessary.
- Wash your hands, tie back your hair and put on your apron.
- Read the recipe right through to ensure that you have all the ingredients and you understand what you will be doing.
- Measure out your ingredients accurately, don't guess. It may be OK for an adult but not when you are first starting to cook.

NOW GO GO GO

Some Cookery Techniques

CORE AND PEEL

Core: To remove the central part of fruit or vegetables that contain the seeds or pips. Normally a corer or small, sharp knife is used for this.

Peel: To remove outer skin from fruit or vegetables.

Beat: Stir food quickly until all the ingredients have blended together. Normally a wooden spoon is used.

Mix: To stir ingredients together but not as vigorously as beating.

Whip: To beat cream with a whisk until thickened.

Whisk: This is beating food with a whisk to incorporate air and to increase the volume.

GRATE, SLICE AND CHOP

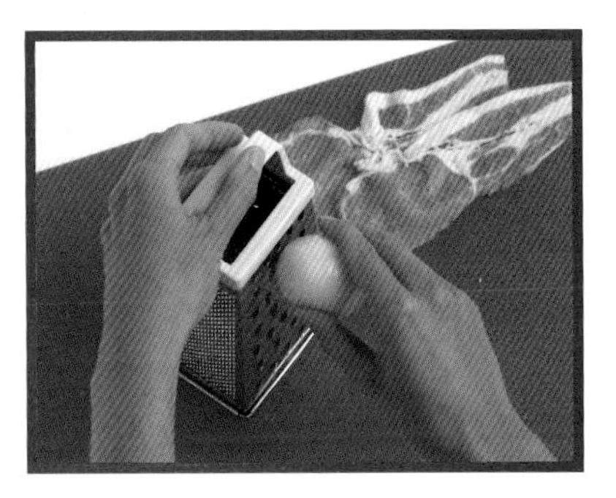

Grate: Normally the coarse side of a grater is used for cheese and vegetables while the middle side is used for grating orange or lemon rind. The very fine side is used for nutmeg.

Slice: To cut food into strips or rings with a small, sharp knife.

Chop: To cut food into small even pieces. Place the food on the chopping board and, holding a small, sharp knife in one hand and steadying the food with the other hand, cut into small pieces. When chopping herbs, remove the stems and place the herbs in a small bowl. Chop using a pair of kitchen scissors.

Marinate: To soak food in a liquid before cooking. This helps to impart flavour as well as to tenderize.

Simmer: To bring liquid to the boil then to reduce the heat and allow the liquid to bubble occasionally.

Garnish: To add herbs or other ingredients at the end of cooking to make the finished dish look more attractive.

Now you have the basic knowledge it's down to you but whatever you cook, just remember

COOKING IS FUN

Safety in the Kitchen

Heat Use oven gloves when handling anything that is hot. Never try to take something out of a hot oven without using oven gloves.

- When using saucepans, hot dishes or baking tins, use both hands and check first that there is nothing in the way of where you are going to place them once you have removed them from the hob or the oven.
- Place hot pans and dishes on a trivet or board. If you feel that a pan or dish is too heavy for you to handle, then ask someone to do it for you.
- When on the hob, keep pan handles turned away from you. Angle them to the side and not over the cooker rings which, if turned on, will heat the handles making them too hot to handle.
- Do not overfill saucepans as they will then be too heavy to lift. There is also the danger that the contents may boil over if the pan is filled close to the brim.
- Call an adult immediately if a fire breaks out. DO NOT try to deal with it yourself.
- Do not be tempted to test for heat by placing your hand or fingers on or in anything that may be hot.
- Turn off the cooker, microwave and any electrical implements that have been used as soon as you have finished with them.
- As well as informing an adult when you are beginning to cook you must also tell them when you have finished so they can check that electrical implements are safely turned off.

Chapter One

Burgers Galore

Hawaiian Burger

Serves 4

FOR THE BURGERS
350g (12oz) lean minced beef
1 onion, peeled
25g (1oz) fresh white breadcrumbs
2 tablespoons freshly chopped parsley
salt and pepper
1 (size 4) egg

FOR THE TOPPING
1 tablespoon sunflower oil
1 onion, peeled
4 floury baps
200g (7oz) can pineapple slices, drained
4 individual cheese slices
few lettuce leaves
Thousand Island Dressing (see page 78)

1 Pre-heat the grill just before cooking and line the grill rack with tin foil. Place the minced beef in a bowl and break up any lumps with a fork. Grate the onion as described on page 19 and add to the bowl with the breadcrumbs, chopped parsley and salt and pepper.

2 Beat the egg, then add to the bowl and mix well, bringing the mixture together to form a ball in the centre of the bowl.

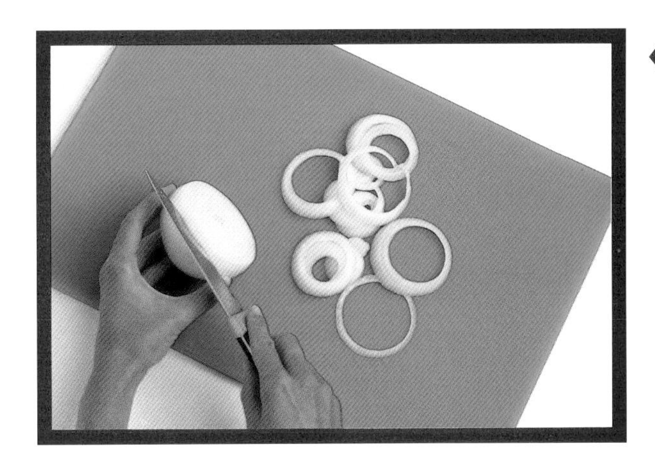

4 Just before cooking the burgers, **slice the onions** into rings and **heat the oil** in a frying pan. **Cook the onions** for 5–8 minutes or until softened. Drain on absorbent kitchen paper. **Cook the burgers** under the preheated grill for 4–5 minutes on each side then drain on absorbent kitchen paper.

5 **Split the baps and toast lightly**. Place a lettuce leaf on to the bap base, then top with a burger and cover with the cooked onions, a pineapple ring and then a cheese slice. **Place under the grill** for about two minutes or until the cheese begins to melt. Cover with the bap lid and serve with the Thousand Island Dressing.

3 Place the mixture on to a chopping board and shape into four round burgers. Place on a plate, cover and chill in the refrigerator for 30 minutes.

Chicken and Corn Burger

Serves 4

FOR THE BURGERS

350g (12oz) minced chicken
1–2 garlic cloves, peeled
6 spring onions
50g (2oz) fresh white breadcrumbs
grated rind 1 small orange
1 teaspoon ground cinnamon
salt and pepper
50g (2oz) canned sweetcorn
1 (size 4) egg, beaten
1–2 teaspoons sunflower oil
4 brown baps

FOR THE TOPPING

few baby spinach leaves, lightly rinsed
1 large tomato
4 tablespoons Corn Relish (see page 94)

1 **Pre-heat the grill** and line the rack with foil. Place the minced chicken in a bowl and break up any lumps with a fork. Crush the garlic in a garlic crusher. Add to the chicken.

2 **Trim off** and discard the root and some of the dark green part of the spring onions and **chop the remainder finely.**

3 Add the spring onions to the bowl with the breadcrumbs, orange rind, ground cinnamon and salt and pepper.

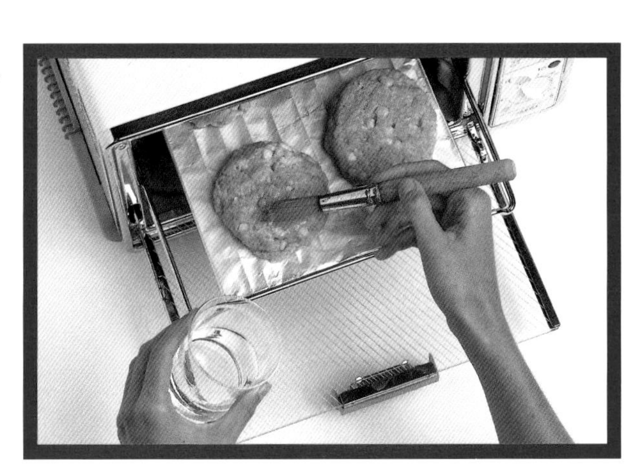

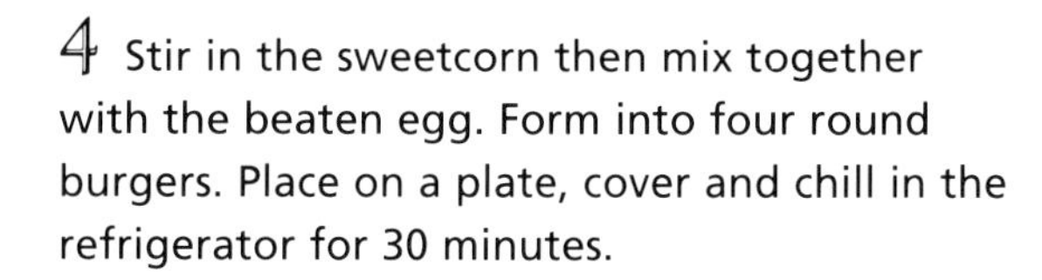

4 Stir in the sweetcorn then mix together with the beaten egg. Form into four round burgers. Place on a plate, cover and chill in the refrigerator for 30 minutes.

5 Brush the chilled burgers with a little oil then **place under the grill** and **cook for 5–6 minutes** on each side. Drain on absorbent kitchen paper.

6 **Split the baps and toast lightly.** Arrange a few spinach leaves over each bap base and cover with a cooked burger. **Slice the tomato** and place over the burger then spoon over a little of the Corn Relish. Place the lid in position and serve.

Turkey and Red Pepper Burger

Serves 4

FOR THE BURGERS

350g (12oz) minced turkey
1 small onion, peeled and grated
1 small red pepper
1 small cooking apple
2 tablespoons freshly chopped parsley
salt and pepper
50g (2oz) fresh white breadcrumbs
1 (size 4) egg, beaten

FOR THE TOPPING

1 red pepper
1 onion, peeled
2 tablespoons sunflower oil
4 granary baps
few lettuce leaves
2–3 tablespoons Barbecue Sauce (see page 85)

1 **Pre-heat the grill** and line the grill rack with tin foil. Place the minced turkey in a mixing bowl and break up any lumps with a fork. Stir in the grated onion.

2 **Cut the top off the pepper** and take out and discard the seeds and the pithy membrane that the seeds are attached to. **Chop finely** and add to the turkey.

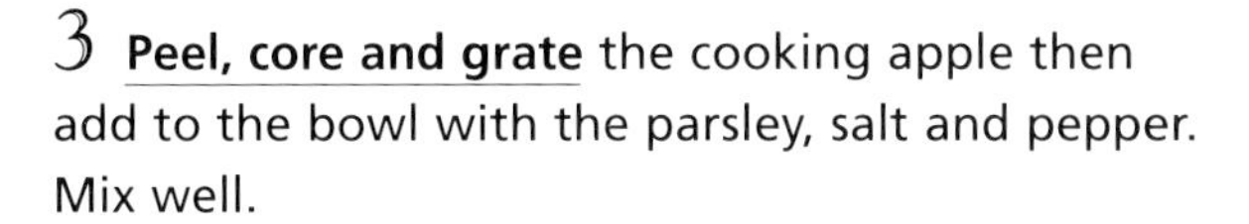

3 **Peel, core and grate** the cooking apple then add to the bowl with the parsley, salt and pepper. Mix well.

4 Add the breadcrumbs and beaten egg to the mixture and then form into four round burgers. Place on a plate, cover and chill for at least 30 minutes in the refrigerator.

5 Meanwhile, deseed the red pepper as previously described then **slice thinly. Thinly slice the onion. Heat the oil** in a frying pan then **gently cook** the pepper and onion for 5–7 minutes or until softened. Drain on absorbent kitchen paper.

6 **Cook the turkey burgers** under the preheated grill for 5–6 minutes on each side then drain on absorbent kitchen paper.

7 **Split the baps and toast lightly**. Arrange a few lettuce leaves on the base of the baps and top with the cooked burgers. Spoon over the cooked pepper and onion.

8 Add the Barbecue Sauce. Place the bap lid in position and serve.

Classic Beefburger

Serves 2

FOR THE BURGERS

350g (12oz) lean beef, such as chuck or braising beef
1 small onion, peeled and grated
salt and pepper
1–2 teaspoons sunflower oil

FOR THE TOPPING

2 onions
1–2 tablespoons sunflower oil
2 burger baps
2–3 tablespoons tomato ketchup or relish

1 **Pre-heat the grill** and line the grill rack with foil just before cooking the beefburgers. Ask your butcher to finely mince the beef for you. (Alternatively use lean minced beef, from the supermarket.) Place the beef in a large mixing bowl and break up any lumps with a fork.

2 **Peel the onion** leaving the root on. Then, using the coarse side of the grater, **grate the onion**. Place the grated onion into the bowl and add salt and pepper to taste.

3 Mix all the ingredients together with your hands then place the mixture on to a clean chopping board.

4 Shape the mixture into two round cakes. (You will find it easier if you slightly dampen your hands before shaping.) Place on a plate, cover and chill in the refrigerator for at least 30 minutes. Brush with a little oil then **place under the preheated grill** and cook for 4–5 minutes on each side or until cooked to personal preference. Drain on absorbent kitchen paper.

5 Meanwhile, **peel and slice the onions** and **heat the oil** in a frying pan. **Cook the onions**, for 6–8 minutes, stirring occasionally with a wooden spatula, or until cooked. Drain on absorbent kitchen paper.

6 **Split the baps and toast lightly** and place the cooked beef burgers on top.

7 Cover with the cooked onions and spoon over a little tomato ketchup. Place the bap lid in position and serve.

Minty Lamb Burger

FOR THE BURGERS
350g (12oz) lean minced lamb
1 small onion, peeled and grated
1–2 garlic cloves, peeled and crushed
50g (2oz) no-need-to-soak apricots
grated rind 1 small orange
2 tablespoons freshly chopped mint
salt and pepper
50g (2oz) fresh brown breadcrumbs

FOR THE TOPPING
4 brown baps
few lettuce leaves, rinsed lightly
small piece cucumber, peeled and sliced
3–4 tablespoons Tomato Relish (see page 76)

1 **Pre-heat the grill** just before cooking the burgers and line the grill rack with tin foil. Place the lamb in a mixing bowl and break up any lumps with a fork. Add the grated onion with the crushed garlic and mix well.

2 **Chop the apricots** into tiny pieces then stir into the mixture with the orange rind, chopped mint and salt and pepper.

4

3 Add the breadcrumbs then mix together and form into four round burgers. Place on a plate, cover and chill for at least 30 minutes.

4 **Cook the burgers** under the preheated grill for five minutes on each side. Drain on absorbent kitchen paper. **Split the burgers and toast lightly**. Cover with the lettuce leaves. Arrange half of the cucumber slices on the lettuce and top with the cooked burgers.

Arrange remaining cucumber on top of the burgers, spoon over the Tomato Relish and place the bap lid in position. Serve.

Pork and Apple Burger

Serves 4

FOR THE BURGERS
350g (12oz) lean minced pork
2 garlic cloves, peeled and crushed
1 teaspoon ground cumin
1 teaspoon ground coriander
salt and pepper
2 tablespoons freshly chopped sage
1 tablespoon grated lemon rind
50g (2oz) fresh white breadcrumbs
1 (size 4) egg, beaten

FOR THE TOPPING
1 eating apple
1–2 teaspoons melted butter
4 floury baps
1 onion, peeled and thinly sliced
3–4 tablespoons Aurore Dressing (see page 88)

2

1 **Pre-heat the grill** just before cooking the burgers and line the grill rack with tin foil. Place the pork in a mixing bowl and break up any lumps with a fork. Add the crushed garlic, spices, salt and pepper, chopped sage, lemon rind and breadcrumbs and mix well.

2 Add the beaten egg then form into four round burgers. Place on a plate, cover and chill in the refrigerator for at least 30 minutes.

4

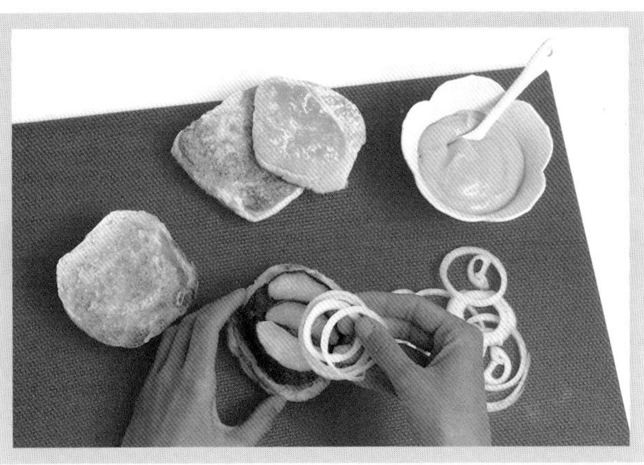

3 **Cook the burgers** under the preheated grill for 5–6 minutes on each side. Drain on absorbent kitchen paper. **Cut the apple into quarters and core. Slice into thick pieces** and brush with the melted butter. **Cook under the grill** for 2–3 minutes or until softened.

4 **Split the baps and toast lightly**. Arrange the cooked burgers on the bap bases and top with the apple slices.

5 Divide the sliced raw onion into rings and place on top of the apple. Spoon over a little Aurore Dressing. Place the bap lids in position and serve.

Veggie Magic

Serves 4

FOR THE BURGERS

420g (14oz) can mixed pulses
2 tablespoons oil
1 onion, peeled and finely chopped
1–2 garlic cloves, peeled and crushed
½ teaspoon chilli powder
2 tablespoons tomato purée
3–4 tablespoons vegetable stock
1½ teaspoons dried mixed herbs
salt and pepper
50g (2oz) wholemeal breadcrumbs
1 tablespoon wholemeal flour

FOR THE TOPPING

4 brown baps
3–4 tablespoon Corn Relish (see page 94)
1 large tomato, sliced
2 tablespoons baked beans
50g (2oz) vegetarian Cheddar cheese, grated

1 **Preheat grill** and line the grill rack with tin foil. Drain the pulses, rinse well and reserve. **Heat one tablespoon of the oil** in a frying pan and **cook the onion and garlic** for five minutes or until softened, stirring frequently.

2 Add the chilli powder and **cook for a further two minutes.** Blend the tomato purée and stock together then stir into the pan.

3 Add the reserved pulses, herbs and seasoning to taste, **bring to the boil** then reduce the heat and simmer for 8–10 minutes.

5 Brush with the remaining oil then place under the preheated grill and **cook for 2–3 minutes** on each side. Drain on absorbent kitchen paper. Split the baps and toast lightly. Spread the Corn Relish on the base and place the cooked burgers on top. Cover with a tomato slice.

6 Top with a few baked beans and grated cheese. **Place under the preheated grill** for two minutes or until the cheese has begun to melt. Place the bap lid in position and serve.

4 **Remove from the heat** and allow to cool. Then pass through a food processor to form a chunky purée. When cool enough to handle, add the breadcrumbs and mix well. Shape into four burgers and coat in the flour. Place on a plate and chill for at least 30 minutes.

Fishy Fun

Serves 4

FOR THE BURGERS

350g (12oz) firm white fish fillets, such as cod or haddock
1 bay leaf
1 small onion, peeled and sliced
300ml (½pt) milk
1 large potato, about 175g (6oz) in weight
salt and pepper
100g (4oz) peeled prawns, thawed if frozen
2 tablespoons freshly snipped chives
grated rind 1 lemon
1 (size 3) egg, beaten
50g (2oz) dried breadcrumbs
1–2 tablespoons sunflower oil

FOR THE TOPPING

4 white baps
few lettuce leaves
¼ cucumber, thinly sliced
50g (2oz) peeled prawns, thawed if frozen
3–4 tablespoons Aurore Dressing (see page 88)

1 Rinse the fish and place in a large frying pan with the bay leaf and sliced onion. Pour over the milk and **cook for ten minutes** or until tender.

2 Drain the fish and allow to cool. Discard the skin and any bones and, using a fork, flake into pieces. Place in a bowl.

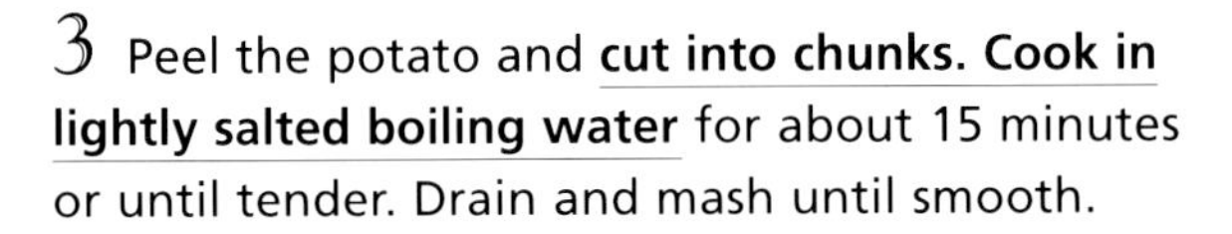

3 Peel the potato and **cut into chunks. Cook in lightly salted boiling water** for about 15 minutes or until tender. Drain and mash until smooth.

4 Add the potato to the fish with salt and pepper to taste. **Roughly chop the prawns** then add to the fish with the snipped chives and grated lemon rind. Mix well together.

5 Place on a board and with slightly dampened hands, shape into 4 burgers. Place on a plate, cover and chill in the refrigerator for at least 30 minutes.

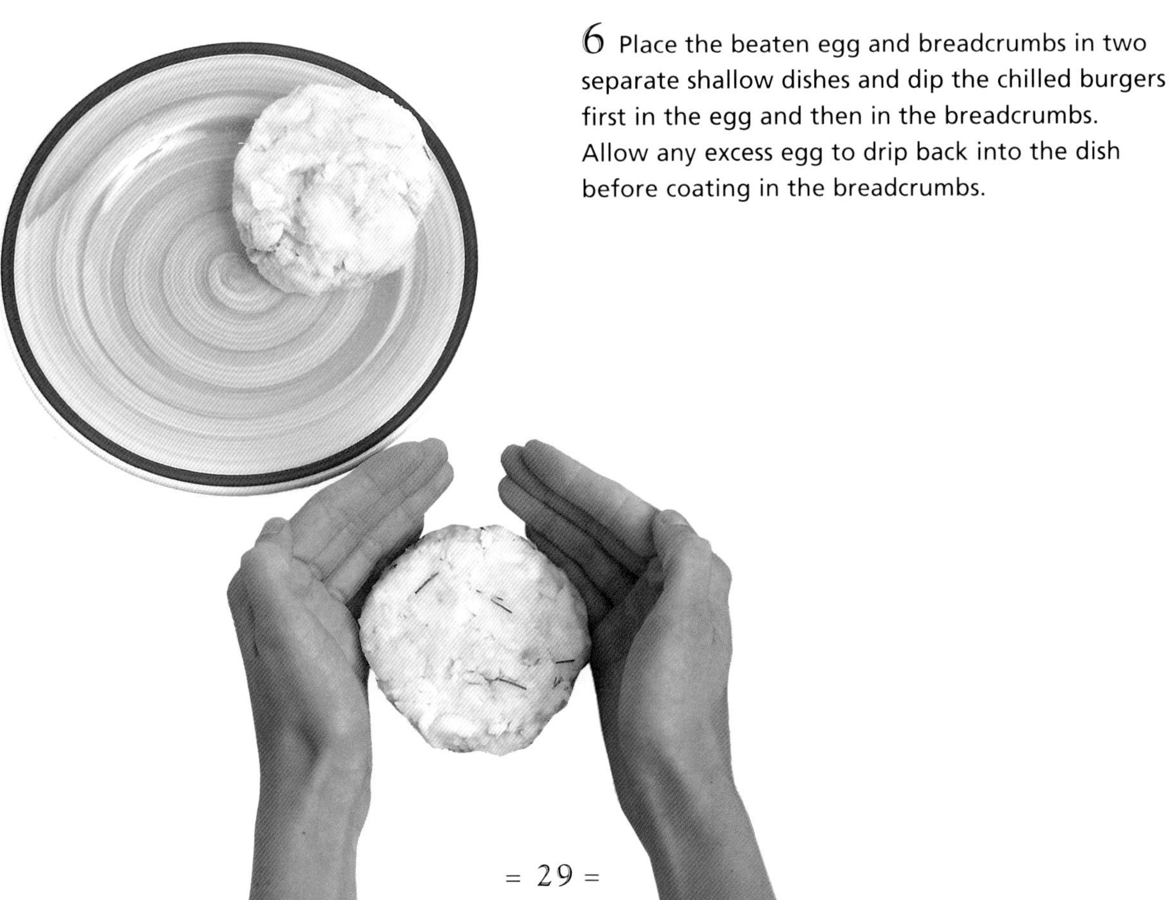

6 Place the beaten egg and breadcrumbs in two separate shallow dishes and dip the chilled burgers first in the egg and then in the breadcrumbs. Allow any excess egg to drip back into the dish before coating in the breadcrumbs.

7 **Heat the oil** in a frying pan then gently cook the burgers for 3–4 minutes on each side or until piping hot and crisp. Drain on absorbent kitchen paper.

8 **Split the baps and toast lightly**. Place a few lettuce leaves on the bap bases, top with a few slices of cucumber then the fish burgers.

9 Place a few more slices of cucumber on top of the fish burgers and arrange a few peeled prawns on top. Then spoon over a little Aurore Dressing. Finish with the bap lid and serve.

Chapter Two

Barking Mad

Classic Hot Dog

Serves 4

YOU WILL NEED

4 frankfurters
1 large onion
1 tablespoon oil
4 hot dog or long finger rolls
1 tablespoon softened butter, optional
2–3 tablespoons tomato ketchup
2–3 tablespoons Hot Mustard Relish (see page 93)

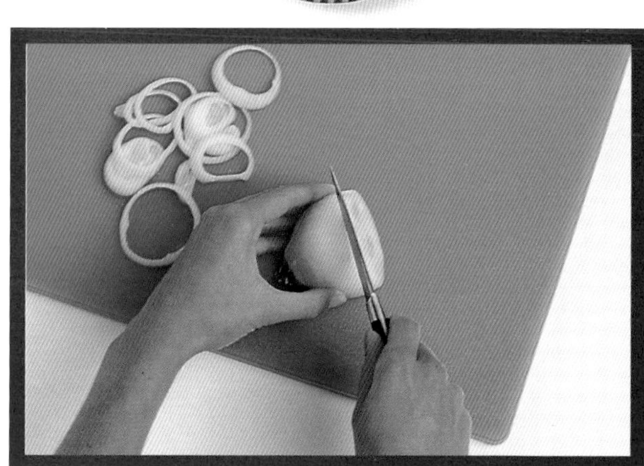

1 Place frankfurters in a pan and cover with either the liquid from the can or fresh water. Place over a gentle heat and **cook for about five minutes**, drain and reserve.

2 Peel the onion and, **using a sharp knife, slice thinly** and divide into rings.

3 **Heat the oil in a frying pan then gently cook the onion** for about five minutes or until softened. Stir frequently during cooking. Drain on absorbent kitchen paper.

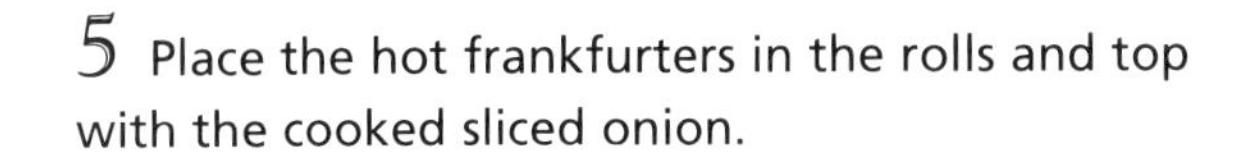

5 Place the hot frankfurters in the rolls and top with the cooked sliced onion.

6 Spoon over the tomato ketchup and Hot Mustard Relish. Serve wrapped in a serviette.

4 Split the rolls and spread with the softened butter.

Salad Supreme

Serves 4

YOU WILL NEED

8 pork chipolata sausages
8 slices streaky bacon, rind removed
4 spring onions
½ red pepper
4 finger rolls or small French sticks
1 tablespoon softened butter
few lettuce leaves
2 tomatoes, sliced
small piece cucumber, sliced
3–4 tablespoons Green Goddess Dressing (see page 86)

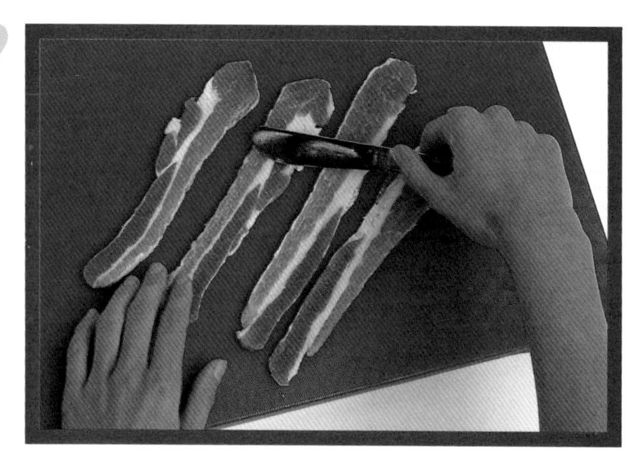

1 **Preheat the grill**. Prick the chipolata sausages lightly with a fork. Place the bacon on a chopping board and with the back of a round bladed knife, gently stretch the bacon.

2 Wrap the bacon round the sausages and secure the ends with a cocktail stick. **Cook under the preheated grill** for about 8–10 minutes. **Turn occasionally during cooking**. Drain on absorbent kitchen paper.

3 **Trim off the root** from the spring onions and most of the dark green part. Discard any seeds from the pepper and **slice into thin strips**.

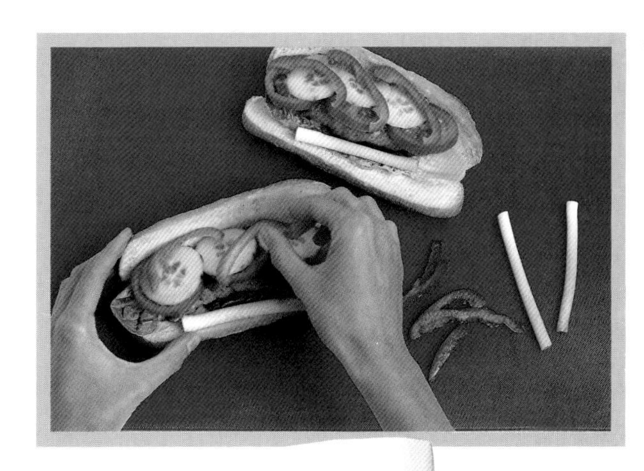

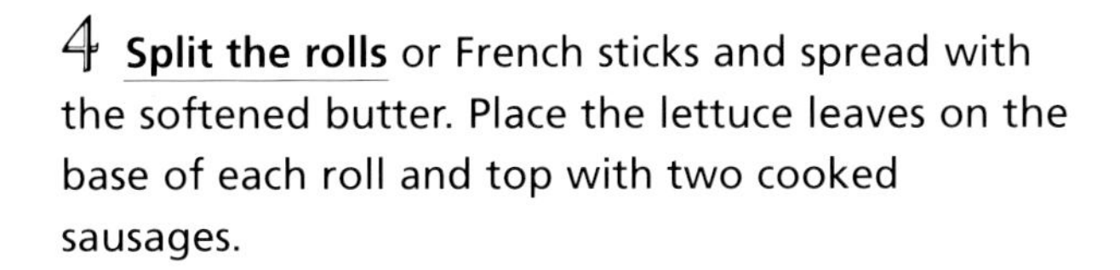

4 **Split the rolls** or French sticks and spread with the softened butter. Place the lettuce leaves on the base of each roll and top with two cooked sausages.

5 Place tomato and cucumber slices on top of the sausages, a spring onion along the side and top with the pepper strips. Spoon over the Green Goddess Dressing and serve.

Fruity Surprise

Serves 4

YOU WILL NEED

4 large pork sausages
4 finger rolls or small French sticks
1 tablespoon softened butter
few lettuce leaves
1 small red apple
1 tablespoon lemon juice
3 tablespoons cranberry sauce

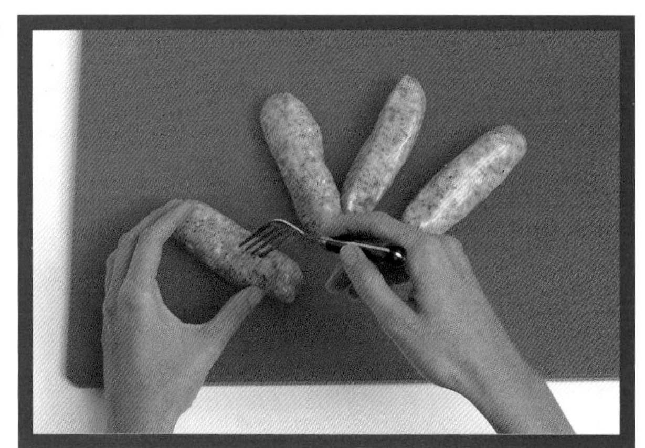

1 **Preheat the grill**. Prick the sausages all over then place in the grill pan. **Cook for about 10 minutes,** occasionally turning the sausages over. **Remove** and drain on absorbent kitchen paper.

2 **Split the rolls** or French sticks and spread with the softened butter.

3 Rinse the lettuce and pat dry. If the leaves are large shred or tear into small pieces. Place on the base of the rolls.

5 Arrange the apple slices on top of the lettuce.

6 Place the cooked sausages on top of the apples and spoon over the cranberry sauce.

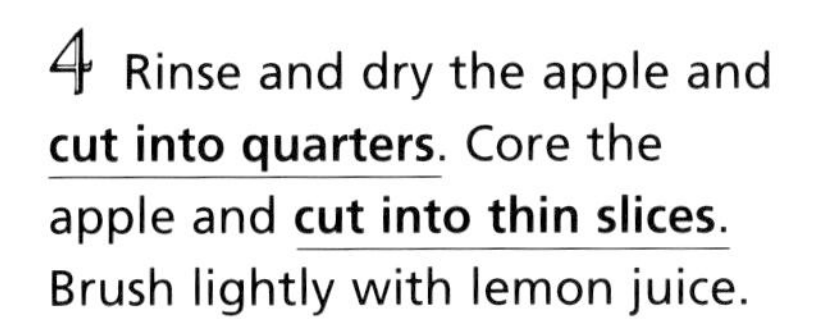

4 Rinse and dry the apple and **cut into quarters**. Core the apple and **cut into thin slices**. Brush lightly with lemon juice.

Hot Chilli Dog

Serves 4

FOR THE HOT DOGS

4 frankfurters

4 finger rolls

1 tablespoon softened butter

FOR THE TOPPING

1 large onion

1–2 garlic cloves

1 red chilli

100g (4oz) mushrooms

1 tablespoon oil

1 tablespoon tomato purée

50g (2oz) Cheddar cheese, grated

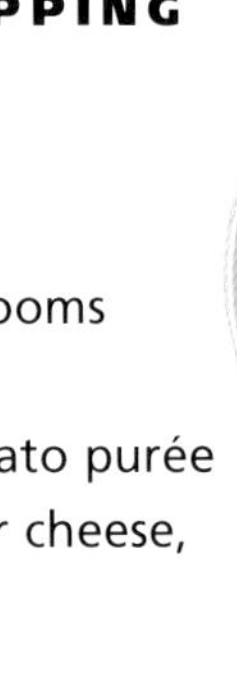

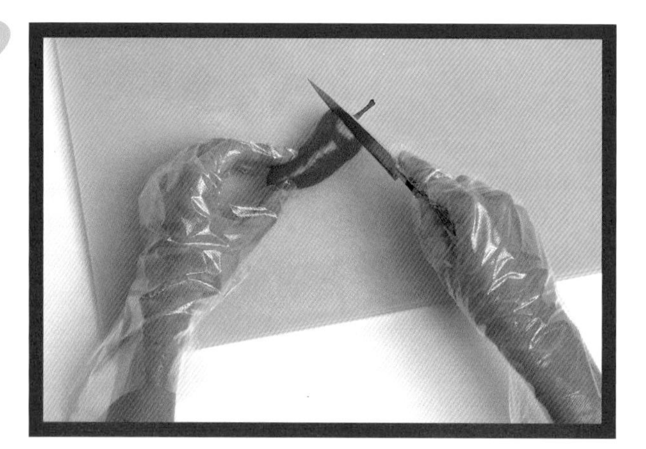

1 Peel and thinly **slice the onion with a small sharp knife.** Peel and crush the garlic using a garlic crusher or pestle and mortar. **Wearing rubber gloves, make a slit** along the length of the chilli and carefully remove the seeds and pithy membrane. **Chop into small pieces. (Remember to take great care when handling chillies and NEVER touch your face until you have removed your rubber gloves or washed your hands if you did not use gloves.)**

2 Wipe the mushrooms to remove loose earth and **slice them thinly**.

3 **Heat the oil** in a frying pan then gently **cook the onion**, garlic and chilli for 4–8 minutes or until softened. Stir frequently during cooking. Add the mushrooms to the pan and **continue to cook** for a further two minutes.

4 Blend the tomato purée with one tablespoon of water then stir into the pan and **cook for three minutes.**

5 **Heat the frankfurters** as previously described on page 32. **Split the rolls** and spread with the softened butter. Place the frankfurters in the rolls and top with the chilli topping.

6 Sprinkle with the cheese and serve immediately.

Chapter Three

Around the World

Tropical Burger

Serves 4

YOU WILL NEED

4 bought or prepared beefburgers
2 ripe plantains or firm bananas
2 tablespoons butter
1 tablespoon oil
1 small ripe pineapple or 200g (7oz) can pineapple slices, drained
1 large tomato
4 burger baps
3–4 tablespoons Thousand Island Dressing (see page 78)

1 **Preheat the grill and cook the beefburgers for four minutes** on each side or until cooked. Drain on absorbent kitchen paper. Peel the plantains or bananas and **cut each into four strips.** Melt the butter and oil in a frying pan and **cook the plantains or bananas for four minutes** on each side or until golden brown. Turn them over during cooking with a fish slice. Drain on absorbent kitchen paper.

2 Place the pineapple on a chopping board. **Cut off** and discard the plume and the base. Stand the pineapple upright on the chopping board and using a sharp knife **carefully cut down** the pineapple and remove the skin.

3 **Cut the pineapple into slices.** Using a small round pastry cutter cut out the hard central core and discard.

4 Rinse and dry the tomato and **slice** into four rings. **Split the baps and toast lightly**. Place the cooked beefburger on the bap base and top with the cooked plantain or banana. Cover with the tomato and then the pineapple.

5 Spoon over the Thousand Island Dressing. Place the lid in position and serve.

The Mexican Connection

Serves 4

YOU WILL NEED

4 prepared or bought chicken burgers
1 garlic clove
1 onion
1 chilli
1 tablespoon oil
¼ iceberg lettuce
2 firm tomatoes
1 ripe avocado
4 burger baps
3–4 tablespoons Salsa (see page 82)
2 tablespoons grated Cheddar cheese

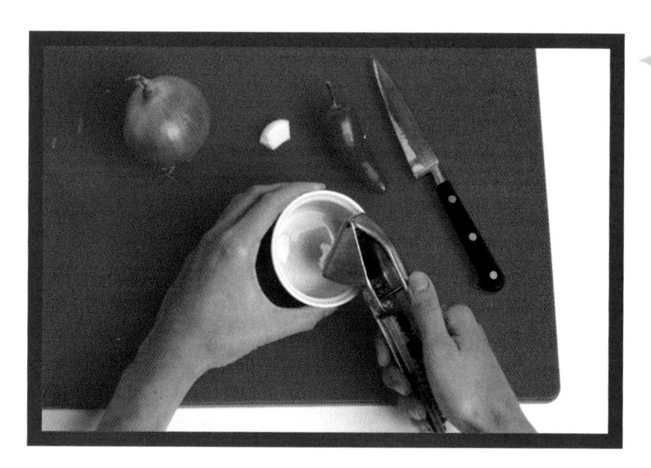

1 **Preheat the grill and cook the chicken burgers** just before required.

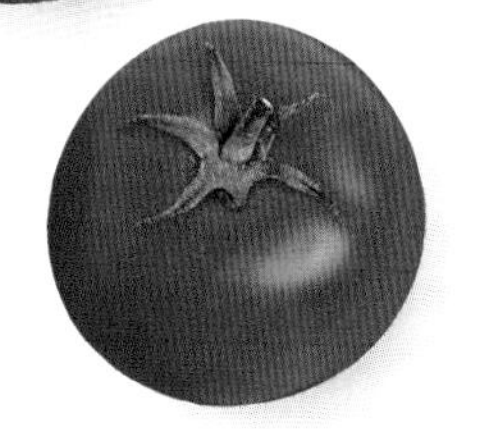

2 Peel and crush the garlic. **Peel and thinly slice** the onion. **Using a pair of rubber gloves, make a slit down the side of the chilli and remove the seeds and pithy membrane with a small sharp knife. Chop into thin strips. (Remember to avoid touching your face while preparing the chilli.)**

3 **Heat the oil** in a frying pan and gently **cook the garlic, onion and chilli** for five minutes or until softened. Drain on absorbent kitchen paper.

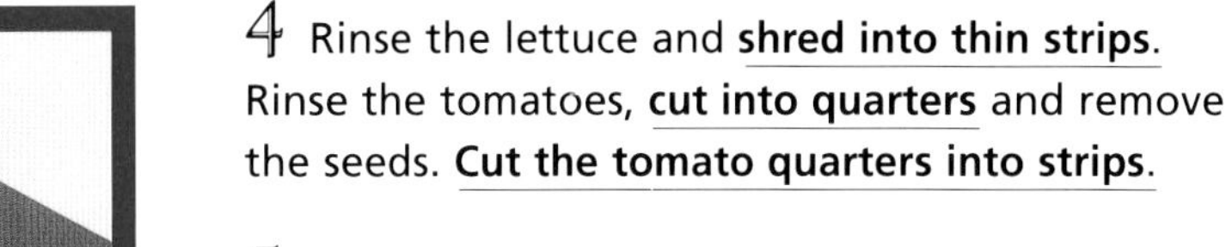

4 Rinse the lettuce and **shred into thin strips**. Rinse the tomatoes, **cut into quarters** and remove the seeds. **Cut the tomato quarters into strips**.

5 **Cut the avocado** in half and discard the stone. Peel then **cut into slices**.

6 **Split the baps and toast lightly**. Place a little of the shredded lettuce on the base of each bap with the tomato strips.

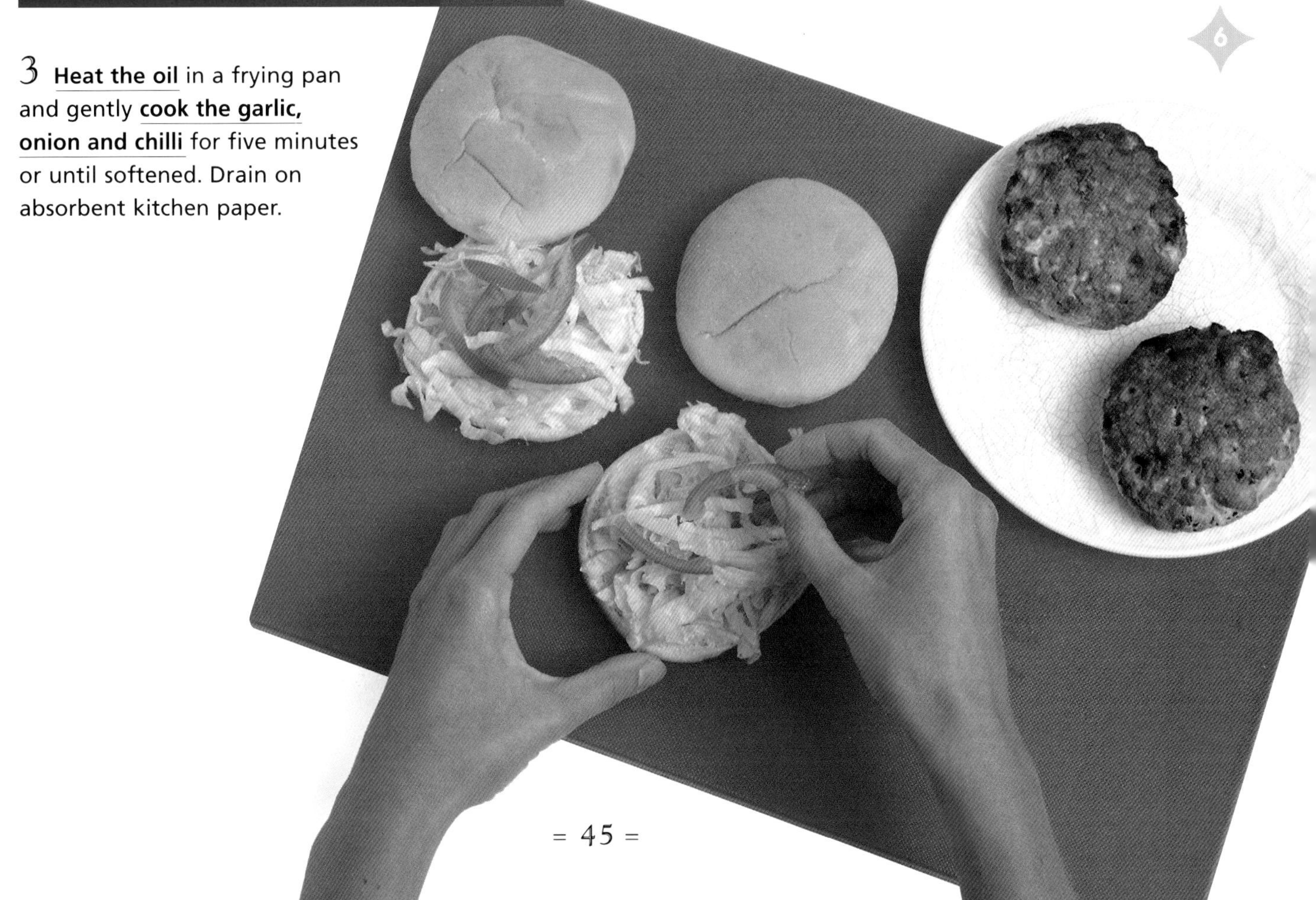

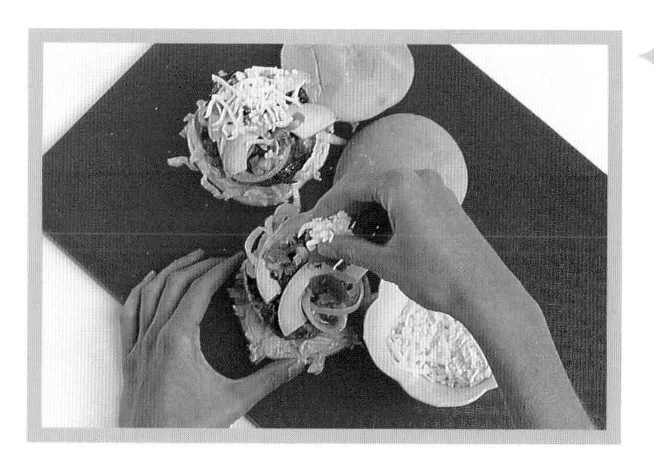

8

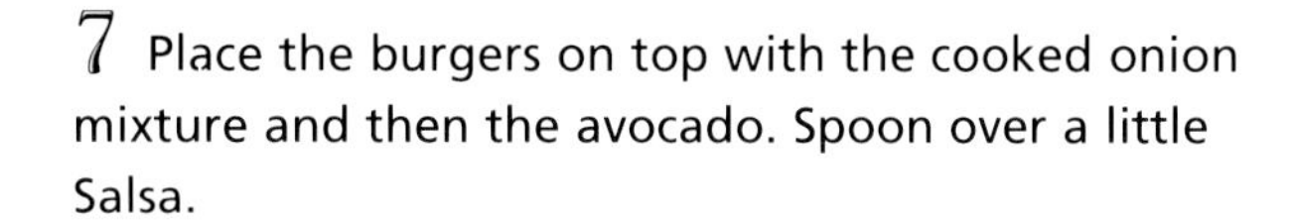

7 Place the burgers on top with the cooked onion mixture and then the avocado. Spoon over a little Salsa.

8 Sprinkle with the cheese. Cover with the lid and serve.

Hot Dog Fajitas

Serves 4

YOU WILL NEED
4 large pork sausages
4–6 spring onions
7.5cm (3in) piece cucumber
½ small red pepper, deseeded
4 wheat tortillas
3–4 tablespoon soured cream
3–4 tablespoon cranberry sauce
Salsa to serve, optional
(see page 82)

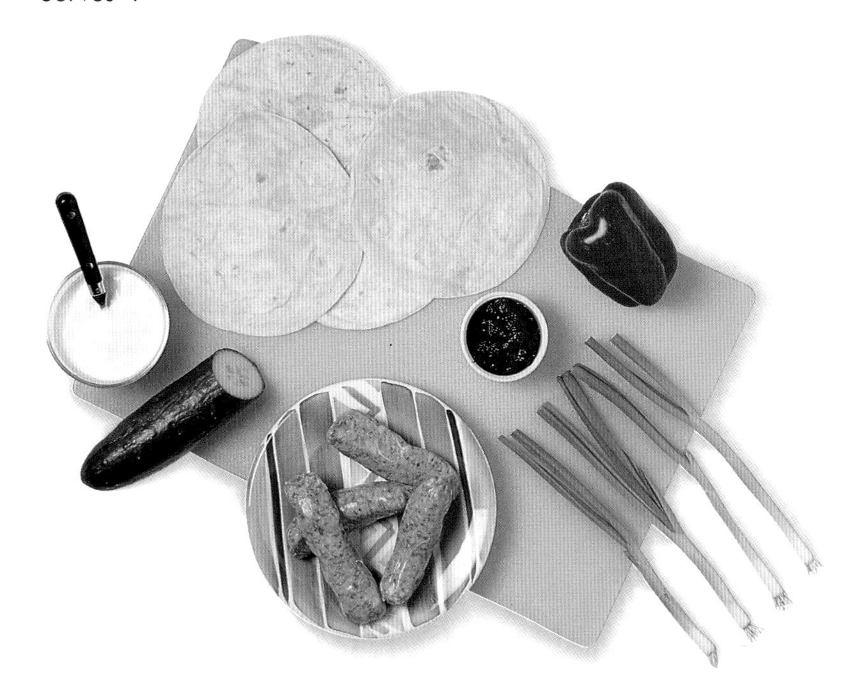

1 Prick the sausages with a fork then **cook under the preheated grill** for ten minutes or until cooked, turning occasionally during cooking. Drain on absorbent kitchen paper.

2 When cool enough to handle, place the cooked sausages on to the chopping board and **slice into thin strips**.

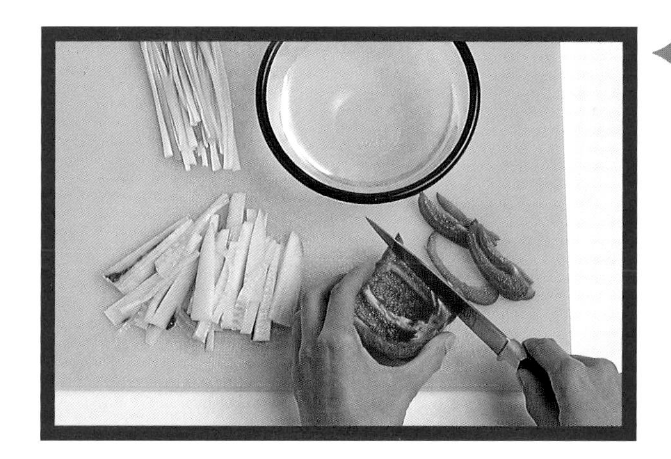

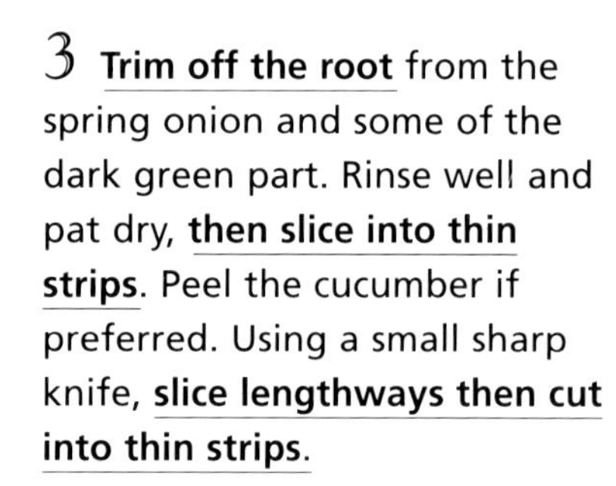

3 **Trim off the root** from the spring onion and some of the dark green part. Rinse well and pat dry, **then slice into thin strips**. Peel the cucumber if preferred. Using a small sharp knife, **slice lengthways then cut into thin strips**.

4 **Cut the pepper** into thin strips. Place in a small bowl and **cover with boiling water** and leave for one minute. Drain and reserve.

5 **Warm the tortillas** for 30 seconds or according to packet instructions.

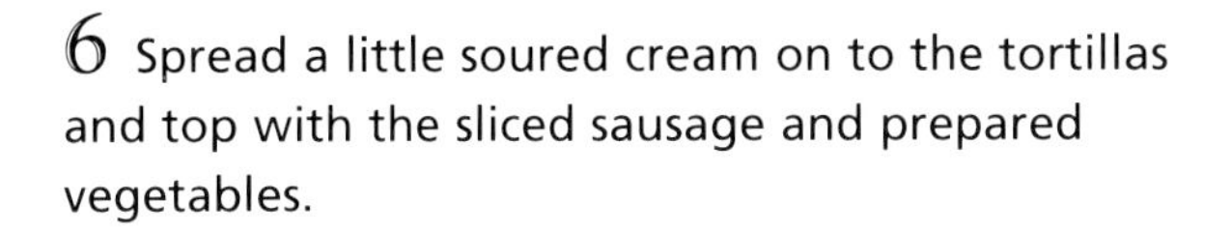

6 Spread a little soured cream on to the tortillas and top with the sliced sausage and prepared vegetables.

7 Top with cranberry sauce to taste and Salsa, if using. Roll up and eat.

Kashmir Trail

Serves 4

YOU WILL NEED

4 prepared or bought beefburgers
1 cooking apple
2 teaspoons melted butter
1 large onion
1–2 garlic cloves
1 tablespoon oil
1–2 teaspoons curry powder
4 white baps
few lettuce leaves, rinsed
2–3 tablespoons mango chutney
1 large tomato, sliced
2–3 tablespoons Curry Relish (see page 90)

1 **Preheat the grill and cook the beefburgers** as previously described, see page 20 or according to packet instructions. Drain on absorbent kitchen paper. **Cut the apple** into quarters then peel and core. **Cut into thick slices**. Brush with the melted butter and **cook under the preheated grill** for 3–5 minutes or until soft. Turn at least once during cooking. Drain on absorbent paper.

2 **Peel and slice** the onion, peel and crush the garlic. **Heat the oil** in a frying pan. **Cook the onion and garlic** for four minutes then sprinkle in the curry powder and continue to cook for a further two minutes. Drain on absorbent kitchen paper.

3 **Split the baps and toast lightly.**

4 Place a few rinsed leaves on the base of each bap and top with the cooked apple slices and beefburgers.

5 Spoon over a little mango chutney then place a slice of tomato on top. Cover with the cooked onion.

6 Add the Curry Relish, if using and place the bap lid in position and serve.

The Chinese Link

Serves 4

YOU WILL NEED

4 prepared or bought chicken burgers
½ small yellow pepper
½ small green pepper
½ small red pepper
6 spring onions
1 small piece of root ginger, peeled and grated or 1 teaspoon freshly minced ginger
1 tablespoon oil
1–2 tablespoons soy sauce
4 floury baps
few Chinese leaves
100g (4oz) fresh bean sprouts
3–4 tablespoons Tomato Relish (see page 76) or extra soy sauce

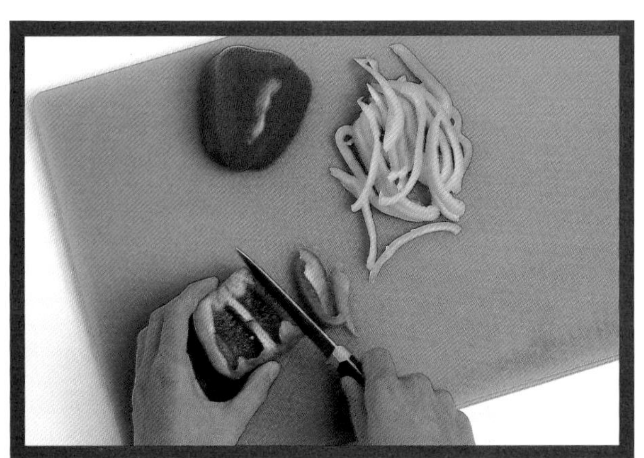

1 **Preheat the grill and cook the chicken burgers** for 8–10 minutes or according to packet instructions just before required. Drain on absorbent kitchen paper. **Deseed all the peppers,** discarding the pithy membrane. Using a small sharp knife, **cut into thin slices**.

2 **Trim off** and discard the root and most of the dark green part from the spring onions, **slice into small pieces.**

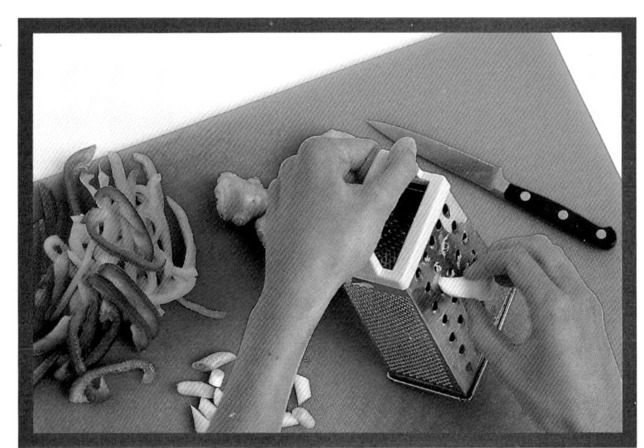

3 **Peel and grate** the ginger.

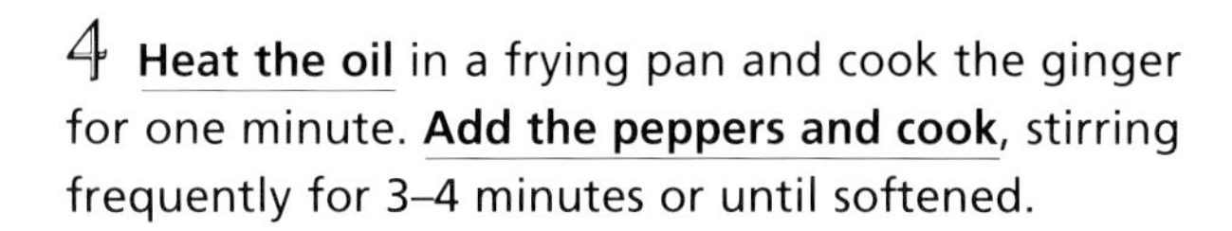

4 **Heat the oil** in a frying pan and cook the ginger for one minute. **Add the peppers and cook**, stirring frequently for 3–4 minutes or until softened.

5 Stir in the spring onions and **cook for one more minute**. **Remove from the heat** and add the soy sauce.

6 **Split the baps and toast lightly**. Rinse the Chinese leaves and **shred into thin strips**. Place the shredded Chinese leaves on the base of the bap and top with a few bean sprouts. Place the burgers on top.

7 Cover with the cooked peppers and the remaining bean sprouts. Spoon over the Tomato Relish or sprinkle with extra soy sauce. Place the bap lid in position and serve.

Chapter Four

Double Whammies

Pork Double Decker

Serves 2

YOU WILL NEED

4 prepared or bought pork burgers
2 rashers back bacon, rind removed
1 small red onion
1 small green pepper
1 tablespoon oil
2 brown baps
few lettuce leaves
2 canned pineapple slices
2 individual cheese slices
2–3 tablespoons Hot Mustard Relish (see page 93)

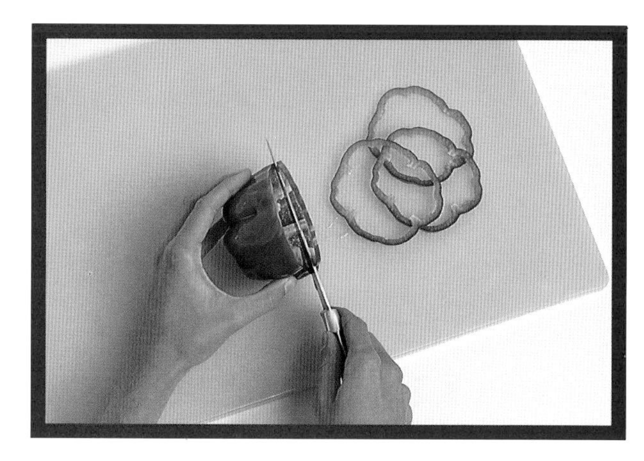

1 **Preheat the grill and cook the burgers** according to packet instructions. Drain on kitchen paper. **Cook the bacon** for two minutes on each side, drain and reserve. **Peel the onion** and place on a chopping board. With a small sharp knife, **cut into thin slices.**

2 **Cut the top off the pepper and with a small sharp knife** remove the seeds and pithy membrane **then cut** into thin rings.

3 **Heat the oil** in a frying pan and **cook the onion and pepper** for five minutes, or until softened. Stir occasionally during cooking. Drain on absorbent kitchen paper.

4

5

6

4 **Split the baps and toast lightly. Rinse and shred the lettuce.**

5 Place some shredded lettuce over the base of the baps and top with one of the cooked burgers. Cover with the cooked onion and pepper mixture.

6 Place the remaining burgers on top with a pineapple slice, bacon rasher and then top with a cheese slice. **Place under the grill** for 2–3 minutes or until the cheese starts to melt. Place the lid in position and serve with the Hot Mustard Relish.

Chicken Whopper

Serves 2

YOU WILL NEED

4 prepared or bought chicken burgers
2 floury baps
baby spinach leaves or few watercress sprigs
7.5cm (3in) piece cucumber
½ small orange pepper
3–4 tablespoons Corn Relish (see page 94)
50g (2oz) mozzarella cheese, grated

1

2

3

1 **Preheat the grill and cook the chicken burgers** for 8–10 minutes or according to the packet instructions. Drain on absorbent kitchen paper.

2 **Split the baps and toast lightly.** Lightly rinse the spinach or watercress and pat dry. Arrange over the bases of the baps.

3 **Peel the cucumber** if preferred, place on a chopping board and with a **small sharp knife, slice thinly. Deseed the pepper** and remove any pithy membrane. **Slice into thin strips.**

4

5

6

4 Place a cooked burger on top of the bap and cover with some of the sliced cucumber and pepper.

5 Top with the remaining burger and then the remaining cucumber and pepper.

6 If liked, spoon over a little of the Corn Relish then sprinkle with the cheese. **Cook under the grill** for 2–3 minutes or until the cheese starts to melt. Place the lid in position and serve with the remaining Relish.

Bean Feast

Serves 2

YOU WILL NEED

4 prepared or bought vegetarian burgers
2 floury baps
few lettuce leaves, such as Little Gem
1 large tomato
3–4 tablespoons refried beans
50g (2oz) vegetarian Cheddar cheese, grated

1

2

3

1 **Preheat the grill and cook the burgers** for 8–10 minutes or according to packet instructions. Drain on absorbent kitchen paper. **Split the baps and toast lightly**. Rinse and pat dry the lettuce leaves.

2 Rinse the tomato and place on a chopping board and with a small sharp knife, **slice thinly**.

3 Place half the lettuce leaves on to the bap bases and top with one of the burgers. Cover with a slice of tomato and then the remaining lettuce and burgers.

4

5

4 Place the refried beans into a small saucepan and **heat for 3–4 minutes**, stirring frequently. Beat gently until smooth and free from lumps.

5 Spoon over the refried beans and sprinkle with the grated cheese.

6 **Place under the grill** for 2–3 minutes or until the cheese starts to melt. Place the lid in position and serve with Corn Relish if desired.

6

Giant Dog

Serves 2

YOU WILL NEED

4 frankfurters
1 large onion
1 courgette
4 ripe tomatoes
50g (2oz) mushrooms
1 tablespoon oil
2 long finger rolls
2 teaspoons softened butter
3–4 tablespoons Blue Cheese Relish (see page 80)

1

2

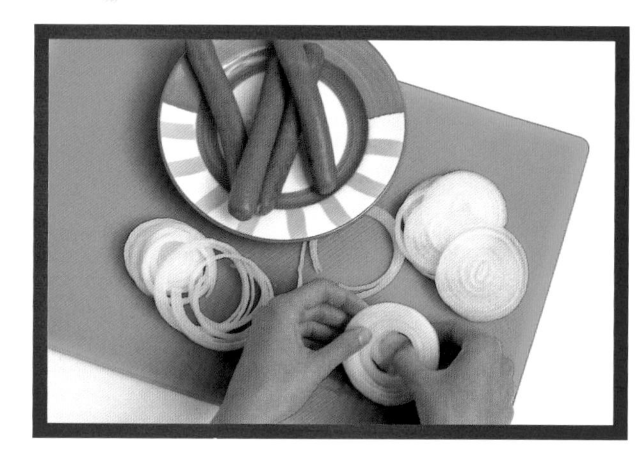

3

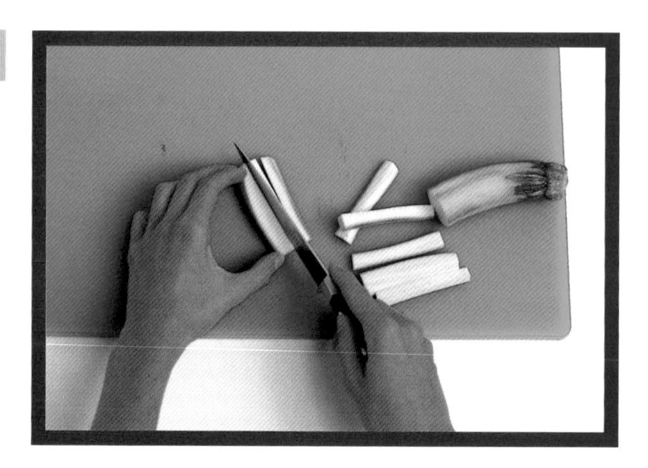

1 Cover the frankfurters with water and **heat for five minutes**, drain and reserve.

2 **Peel the onion**, place on a chopping board and with a **small sharp knife, slice thinly** into rings.

3 **Trim the courgette**, peel if preferred and then place on a chopping board and **cut into strips**.

4

5

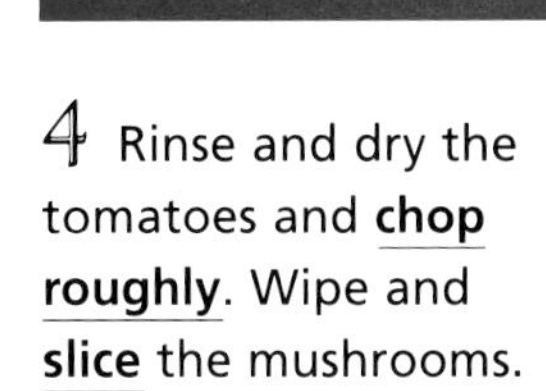

4 Rinse and dry the tomatoes and **chop roughly**. Wipe and **slice** the mushrooms.

5 **Heat the oil** in a frying pan and **cook the onion** for five minutes or until softened. Stir occasionally during cooking. Add the courgette strips and continue to **cook for a further three minutes**.

6

7

6 Add the tomatoes and mushrooms to the pan and **cook for three more minutes**.

7 **Split the rolls** and spread with the softened butter. Place the frankfurters into the rolls and top with the cooked onion mixture and serve with the Blue Cheese Relish.

Chapter Five

Sunny Choice

Sunny Side Up

Serves 4

YOU WILL NEED

4 prepared or bought beefburgers
1 tablespoon oil
4 (size 3) eggs
few lettuce leaves, such as iceberg
1 large tomato
2–3 dill cucumbers
4 burger baps
2–3 tablespoons ketchup or Corn Relish (see page 94)

1

2

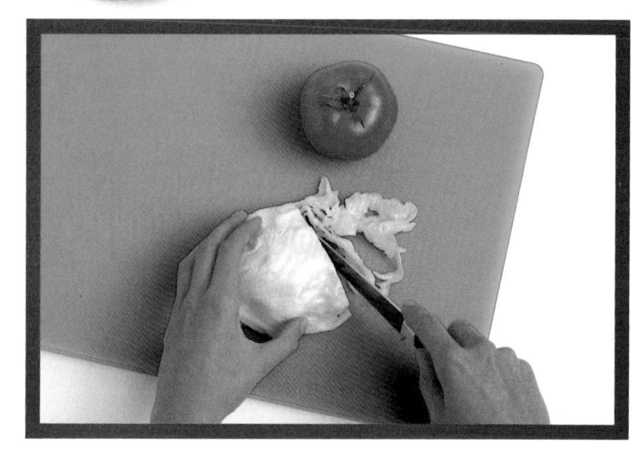

3

1 **Preheat the grill and cook the beefburgers** for 8–10 or according to packet directions. Drain on absorbent kitchen paper. **Heat the oil in a frying pan**. Break an egg into a cup then gently slide into the pan taking care not to break the yolk. **Fry for 4–5 minutes**. Repeat until all the eggs are cooked. (You can do them all at the same time if your pan is large enough.) Drain well.

2 Rinse the lettuce and pat dry **then shred**. Rinse the tomato and **cut into four slices**.

3 **Slice the cucumber into strips. Split the baps and toast.**

4 Place the shredded lettuce on the base of each bap and top with a cooked burger. Arrange the sliced tomato and cucumber on top.

5 Carefully place the cooked egg on the burger and place the top in position. Serve with tomato ketchup or Corn Relish.

Summer Holiday

Serves 4

YOU WILL NEED

8 vegetarian sausages
few lettuce leaves
50g (2oz) seedless grapes
2 ripe pears
1 tablespoon lemon juice
4 finger rolls
2 teaspoons softened butter
8 spring onions
50g (2oz) vegetarian cheese, grated
3–4 tablespoons Aurore Dressing (see page 88)

1

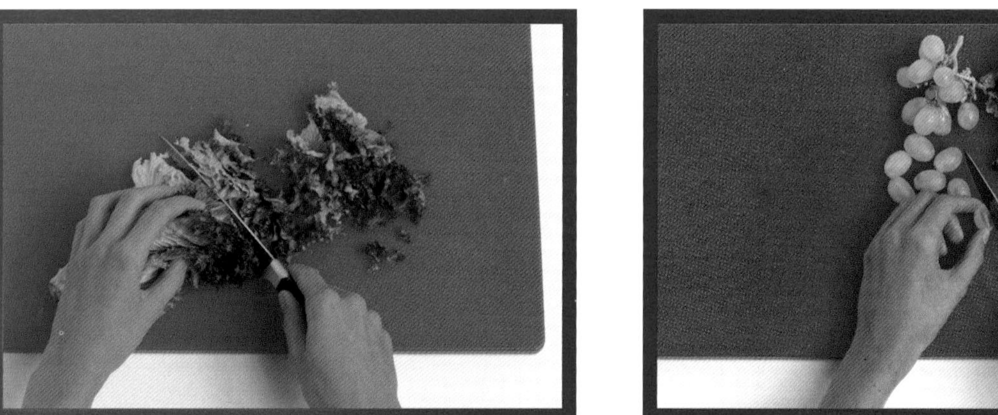

2

3

1 **Preheat the grill and cook the sausages** for 8–10 minutes or according to the packet instructions. Drain on absorbent kitchen paper. Rinse the lettuce, pat dry and **shred finely**.

2 Rinse the grapes and pat dry then **slice in half**.

3 Peel the pears, **cut in half** and remove the core with a teaspoon. **Cut into thin slices**. Brush with lemon juice.

4 **Split the rolls** and spread with the softened butter. Place the shredded lettuce in each roll.

5 Add the sausages with the grapes and pears.

6 **Trim off** the root and most of the dark green part from the spring onion, rinse well. Add the spring onions to the roll and sprinkle with the cheese. Serve with Aurore Dressing if desired.

Neptune's Choice

Serves 4

YOU WILL NEED
- 4 fish burgers
- ¼ iceberg lettuce
- 2–3 dill cucumbers
- 3–4 ripe tomatoes
- 4 burger baps
- 2–3 tablespoons prepared coleslaw
- 2–3 tablespoons Aurore Dressing (see page 88)

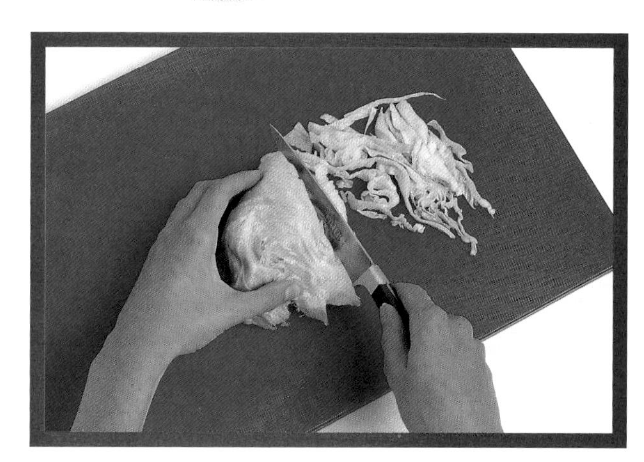

1 **Preheat the grill and cook the fish burgers** for 4–5 minutes on each side or according to packet instructions.

2 Rinse the lettuce and pat dry on absorbent kitchen paper then place on a chopping board and **shred finely**.

3 **Cut the dill cucumbers** thinly into slices.

4 Wipe the tomatoes and **slice thinly.**

5 **Split the baps and toast lightly**. Place the shredded lettuce on the bap bases and cover with the sliced cucumbers and tomatoes.

6 Place the cooked burger on top then spoon over the coleslaw. Pour over a little Aurore Dressing and place the bap lid in position and serve.

Real Fruity Dog

Serves 4

YOU WILL NEED

4 frankfurters
1 satsuma
50g (2oz) seedless grapes
1 kiwi fruit
4 finger rolls
2 teaspoons softened butter
2–3 tablespoons Blue Cheese Relish (see page 80)

1 Place the frankfurters in a saucepan and cover with water. **Bring to the boil** and simmer for 5 minutes. Drain and reserve.

2 Peel the satsuma and divide into segments, discarding as much of the pith as possible. **Cut the segments in half** and place in a small bowl.

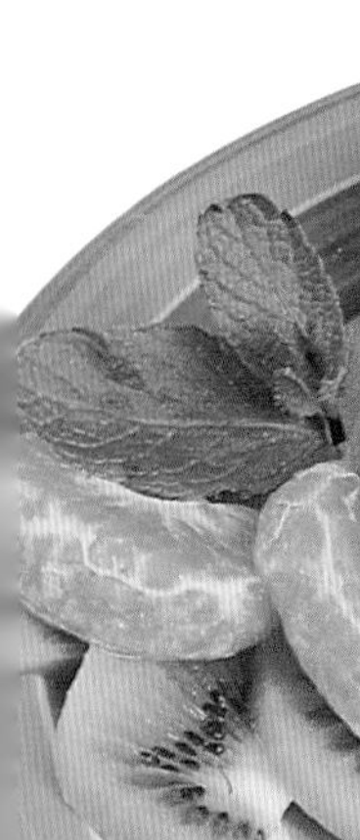

3 Rinse and pat dry the grapes and **cut in half**. Add to the bowl.

4 Peel the kiwi fruit, **chop into small pieces**, add to the fruit and mix lightly together.

5 **Split the rolls** and spread with the softened butter.

6 Place the fruit mixture in the rolls and top with the cooked frankfurters.

7 Spoon a little of the Blue Cheese Relish over and serve.

Chapter Six

Saucy Parade

Tomato Relish

Makes about 300ml (½pt)

YOU WILL NEED

- 1 small onion
- 1–2 garlic cloves
- 2 celery sticks
- 1 small green pepper
- 1 tablespoon oil
- 2 tablespoons tomato purée
- 397g (14oz) can chopped tomatoes
- salt and pepper
- 1 tablespoon Worcestershire sauce
- 1 tablespoon freshly chopped oregano or 1 teaspoon dried

1 **Peel the onion** using a small sharp knife then place on a chopping board and **chop finely**.

2 Peel and crush the garlic in a garlic crusher and add to the onion. **Trim the celery** and wash well under cold water then using a small sharp knife **cut into very small dice**.

3 **Cut the top off** the pepper and remove the seeds and pithy membrane. Rinse and pat dry with absorbent kitchen paper then **chop finely**.

5

4 **Heat the oil** in a frying pan then **gently cook** all the prepared vegetables for 5–8 minutes or until softened. Stir frequently during cooking. When softened, drain the vegetables on absorbent kitchen paper, wipe the pan clean and return the vegetables to the pan.

5 Blend the tomato purée with two tablespoons of water and **stir into the pan** together with the can of tomatoes.

6 Add the salt and pepper to taste with the Worcestershire sauce and chopped oregano then **bring to the boil. Reduce the heat and simmer for 10 minutes,** stirring occasionally, until a thick consistency is reached. **Remove from the heat** and use as required. The Relish will keep if kept covered in the refrigerator for up to one week.

Thousand Island Dressing

Makes about 200ml (7fl oz)

YOU WILL NEED

1 shallot
½ small green pepper
½ small yellow pepper
1 small carrot
6 pitted green olives, optional
150ml/¼pt prepared mayonnaise
1 teaspoon tomato purée
1 tablespoon fresh parsley

1

2

3

1 **Peel the shallot** leaving the root on. Place on a chopping board and **cut into very small dice**. Place in a bowl.

2 **Deseed** both peppers, discarding the pithy membrane and rinse. Pat dry on absorbent kitchen paper. Place on the chopping board and with a small sharp knife, **cut into very small dice**. Add to the shallot.

3 **Peel the carrot and cut off** and discard the top. Using the coarse side of the grater, **grate the carrot** and add to the bowl.

5

6

4 If using the olives, place on the chopping board and **chop finely**, add to the bowl.

5 Stir in the mayonnaise and the tomato purée and mix all the ingredients together.

6 Rinse the parsley lightly and pat dry with absorbent kitchen paper. Snip with scissors until finely chopped. Stir in to the mixture and use as required. Will keep for up to one week, if kept covered in the refrigerator. Sprinkle the top with a little extra chopped parsley before serving.

Blue Cheese Relish

Makes about 200ml (7fl oz)

YOU WILL NEED

2 celery sticks
25g (1oz) walnuts or pecans
1 small eating apple
1 tablespoon lemon juice
50g (2oz) blue cheese such as dolcellate
150ml (¼pt) mayonnaise

1

2

1 **Trim the celery** and wash well under the cold water. Pat dry on absorbent kitchen paper. Place on the chopping board and with a small sharp knife, **cut into small dice**. Place in a bowl. Place the nuts on to the chopping board and **chop finely**. Add to the bowl.

2 Rinse the apple and pat dry. **Cut into quarters** and discard the core. **Chop into small pieces** and sprinkle with the lemon juice.

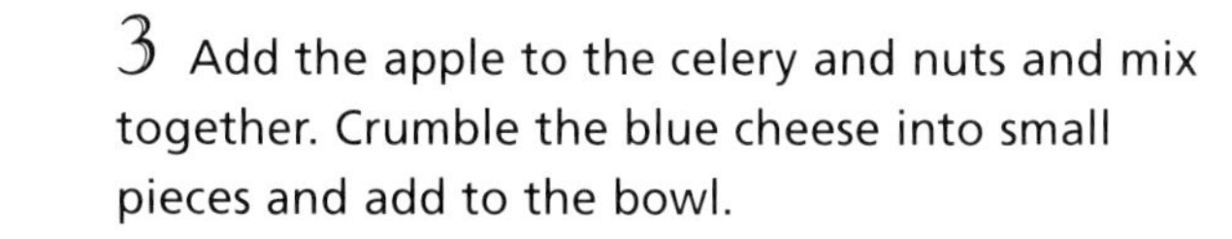

3 Add the apple to the celery and nuts and mix together. Crumble the blue cheese into small pieces and add to the bowl.

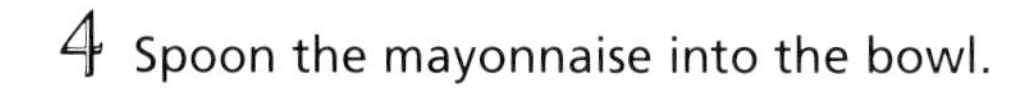

4 Spoon the mayonnaise into the bowl.

5 Mix lightly together. Use as required. Will keep for 2–3 days if kept covered in the refrigerator.

Salsa

Makes about 150ml (¼pt)

YOU WILL NEED

4 spring onions
1 garlic clove
1 red chilli
¼ small cucumber
4 ripe tomatoes
1–2 teaspoons clear honey, warmed
salt and pepper
1 tablespoon white wine vinegar
1 tablespoon lemon or lime juice
1 tablespoon freshly chopped coriander

1 Trim off the root and most of the dark green part from the spring onions. Wash well under cold water, pat dry then chop very finely. Place in a bowl. Peel and crush the garlic with a garlic crusher and add to the spring onions.

2 **Wearing a pair of rubber gloves, make a slit down the side of the chilli and remove the seeds and pithy membrane. Rinse lightly and pat dry. Chop finely and add to the spring onions. (Remember not to touch your face when preparing chillies.)**

4

3 Peel the cucumber and **cut into very small dice**. Squeeze out any excess moisture on absorbent kitchen paper then add to the spring onions.

4 Make a cross on the top of each tomato and place in a clean bowl. **Cover with boiling water** and leave for two minutes. Drain carefully.

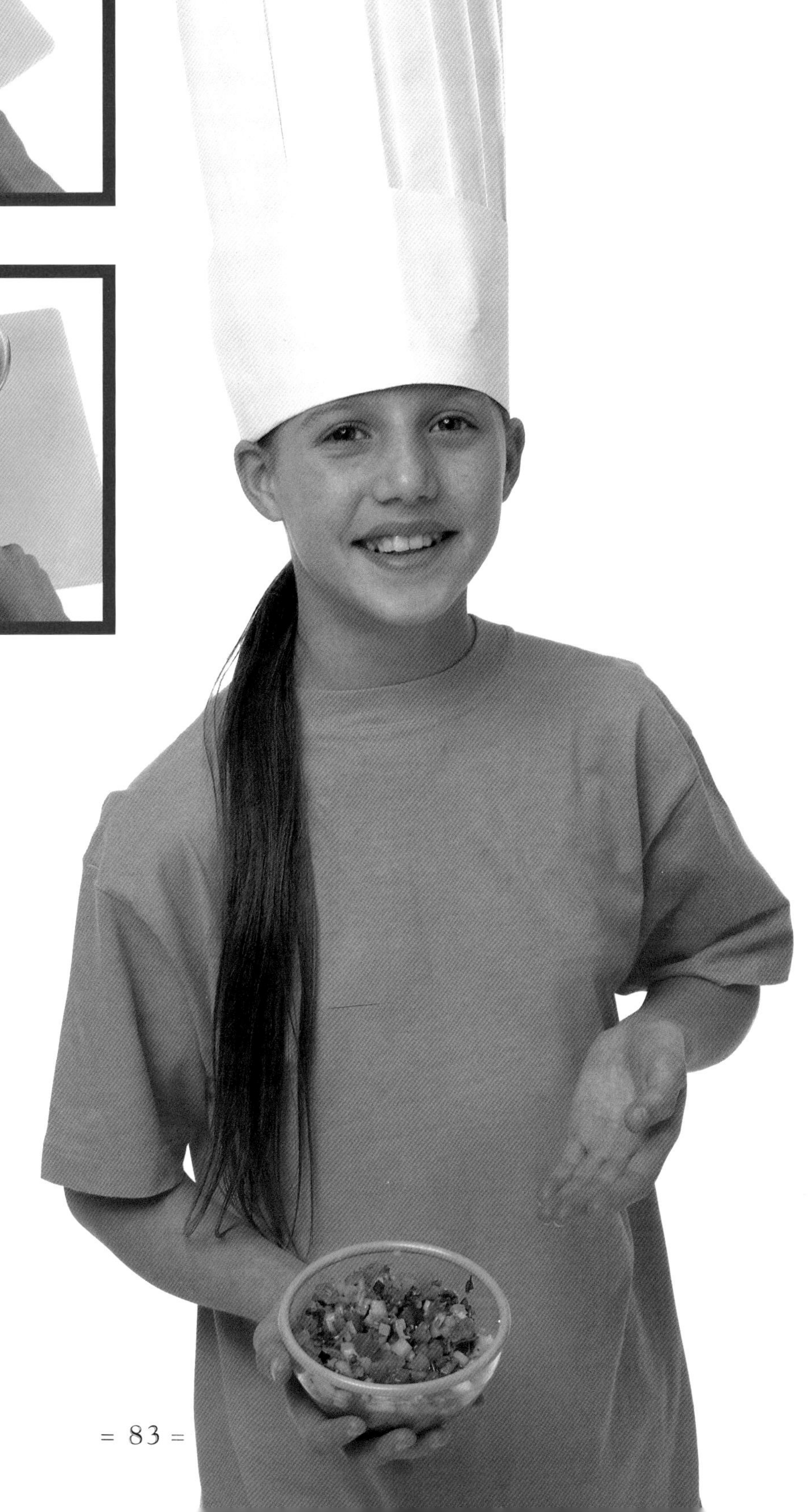

5

6

5 When cool enough to handle, strip off the skin. **Cut into quarters** and remove the seeds. **Dice finely** and pat out any excess moisture with absorbent kitchen paper. Add to the spring onions.

6 Add the honey with salt and pepper to taste, the vinegar and lemon or lime juice.

7 Stir in the coriander and mix all the ingredients lightly together. Cover and leave in a cool place for at least 30 minutes to allow the flavours to develop. Use as required. The Salsa will keep for up to one week if kept covered in the refrigerator.

7

Barbecue Sauce

Makes about 150ml (¼pt)

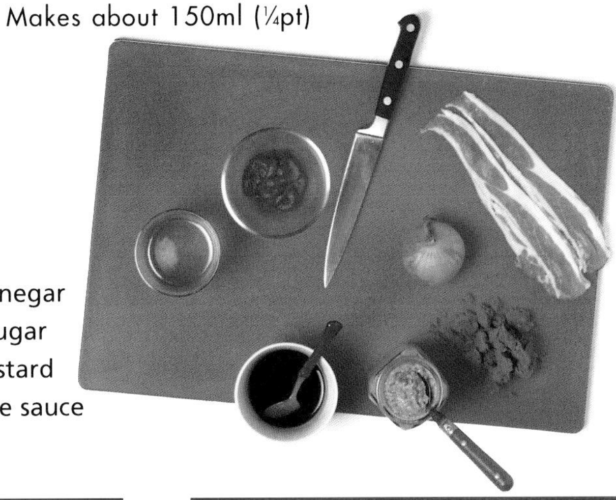

YOU WILL NEED
1 onion
2 rashers smoked bacon
1 teaspoon oil
1 teaspoon tomato purée
2 tablespoons white wine vinegar
25g (1oz) dark soft brown sugar
2 teaspoons wholegrain mustard
2 tablespoons Worcestershire sauce

1

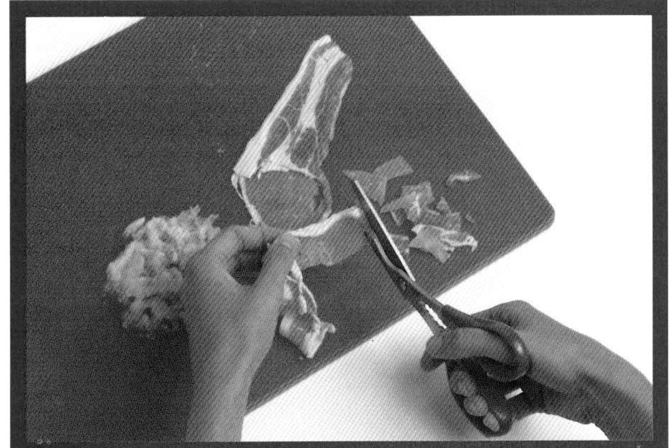

2

3

1 **Peel the onion**, leaving the root on, **then grate** on the coarse side of the grater. Discard any rind and cartilage from the bacon and **chop into small pieces**.

2 **Heat the oil** in a pan then add the bacon and **cook over a gentle heat** until the fat starts to run out. Add the onion and continue to **cook gently for three minutes**.

3 Blend the remaining ingredients together with 150ml/¼pt of water then stir into the pan. **Bring to the boil, reduce the heat and simmer uncovered for 10 minutes**. Stir occasionally during cooking. The Barbecue Sauce will keep for up to one week, covered, in the refrigerator.

Green Goddess

Makes about 200ml (7fl oz)

YOU WILL NEED

1 bunch watercress
7.5cm (3in) piece cucumber
4 spring onions
½ small green pepper
150 ml (¼pt) prepared mayonnaise

1 Pick the watercress over discarding any tough stems or damaged and bruised leaves. Rinse well under the cold water and shake dry in a salad spinner. **Place on a chopping board and finely chop**. Place in a bowl.

2 **Peel the cucumber and cut** into long slices about 6mm (¼in) thick. Cut each slice into thin sticks and then into small dice. Add to the watercress.

3 **Trim off the root** and most of the dark green part from the spring onions. Rinse well under cold water. Place on the chopping board and **chop finely**. Add to the watercress.

4 **Deseed** the pepper and rinse well. Pat dry with absorbent kitchen paper then place on the chopping board and **finely chop**. Add to the bowl and mix all the ingredients together.

5 Spoon in the mayonnaise and mix together. Use as required. Will keep for up to 3–4 days, if stored covered, in the refrigerator.

Aurore Dressing

Makes about 300ml (½pt)

YOU WILL NEED
300ml/½pt semi-skimmed milk
1 small onion
3 whole cloves
1 small carrot
2 bay leaves
few parsley sprigs
50g (2oz) butter
25g (1oz) plain flour
1 tablespoon tomato purée
salt and pepper

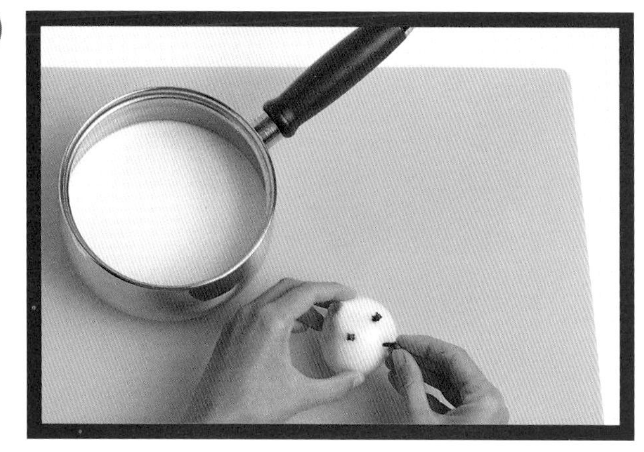

1 Pour the milk into a saucepan. **Peel the onion** and stud with the whole cloves. Place in the saucepan.

2 **Peel the carrot** and add to the pan with the bay leaves and parsley sprigs. Place over a gentle heat and **bring to just below boiling point.**

3 **Remove from the heat,** cover and leave for 30 minutes for the flavour to infuse in the milk. Strain the milk and reserve.

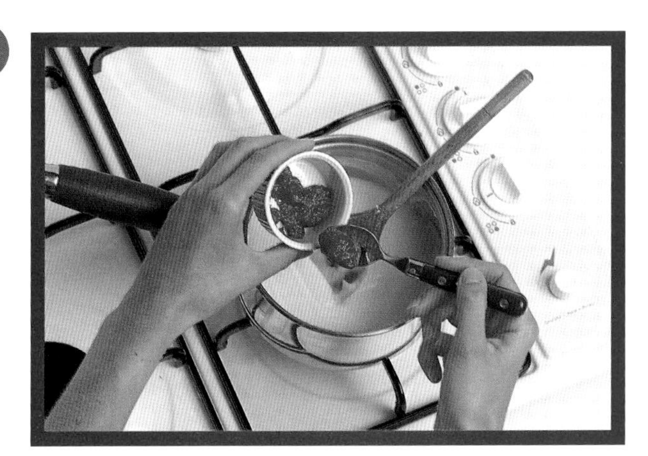

4 **Melt 25g (1oz) of the butter** in a clean pan then stir in the flour. **Cook over a gentle heat for one minute** then gradually stir in the reserved milk.

5 **Cook, stirring until the sauce thickens** and coats the back of the spoon.

6 Stir the tomato purée into the sauce and when blended, **remove from the heat**.

7 Whisk the remaining butter into the sauce with seasoning to taste. Use as required. Will keep for 2–3 days, if kept covered in the refrigerator. Do not re-heat as the sauce will separate and curdle. Whisk before using.

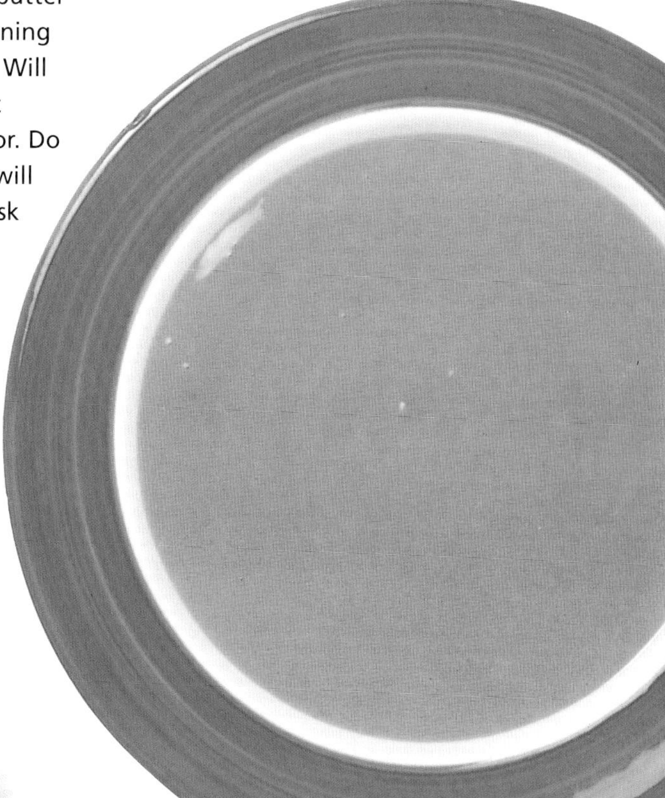

Curry Relish

Makes about 150ml (¼pt)

YOU WILL NEED

1 small onion
2 celery sticks
1 small red pepper
1 tablespoon oil
2–3 teaspoons curry powder
1 teaspoon curry paste
50g (2oz) no-need-to-soak apricots
2–3 tablespoons stock or water
1 tablespoon freshly chopped coriander or parsley
2–3 tablespoons yoghurt

1 **Peel the onion** and place on a chopping board and, with a small sharp knife, **chop finely**.

2 **Trim the celery** then wash well under cold water. Place on the chopping board and **cut into very small dice**.

3 **Cut off the top** from the pepper and remove the seeds and pithy membrane. Rinse lightly and pat dry with absorbent kitchen paper. Place on the chopping board and **chop finely**.

4

5

6

4 **Heat the oil** in a frying pan then **gently cook the prepared** vegetables for five minutes or until softened. Stir frequently during cooking.

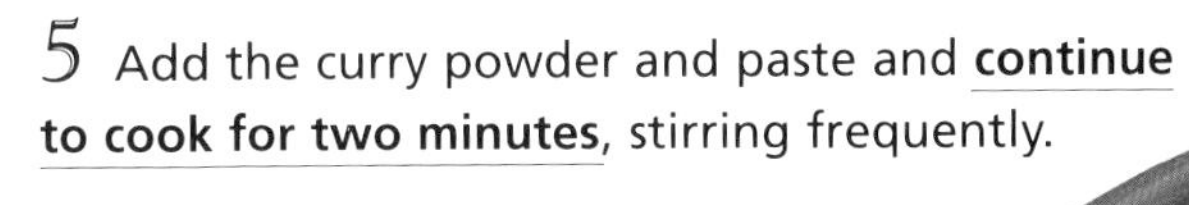

5 Add the curry powder and paste and **continue to cook for two minutes**, stirring frequently.

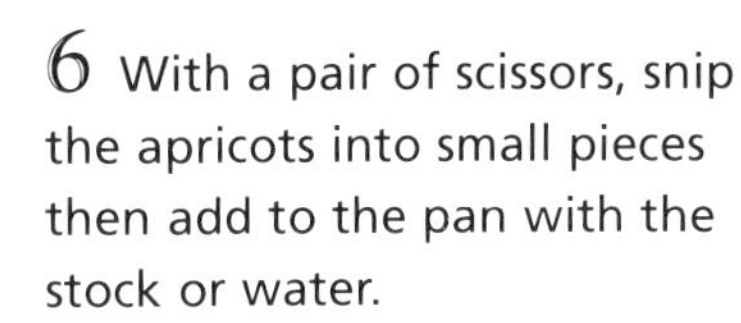

6 With a pair of scissors, snip the apricots into small pieces then add to the pan with the stock or water.

7 **Simmer for five minutes** or until the liquid has evaporated. **Remove from the heat**, cool, then stir in the chopped coriander.

8 Finally, stir in the yoghurt. Use as required. Will keep in the refrigerator if kept covered for 3–4 days.

Hot Mustard Relish

Makes about 150ml (¼pt)

YOU WILL NEED
1 small onion, peeled
1 teaspoon oil
2–3 teaspoons dark soft brown sugar
150ml (¼pt) vegetable stock
3 tablespoons white wine vinegar
1–2 tablespoons wholegrain mustard
salt and pepper
2 teaspoons cornflour

1 **Chop the onion into very small dice. Heat the oil** in a saucepan, add the onion and **cook for five minutes**, stirring. Add the sugar and the stock and **cook over a gentle heat,** stirring frequently until the sugar has dissolved.

2 Blend the vinegar and mustard together then stir into the pan and add seasoning to taste. **Cook gently for five minutes**, stirring occasionally.

3 Blend the cornflour with one tablespoon of water and stir into the pan. **Cook, stirring until the mixture thickens**. Use either warm or cold as required. Will keep for up to one week, covered, in the refrigerator.

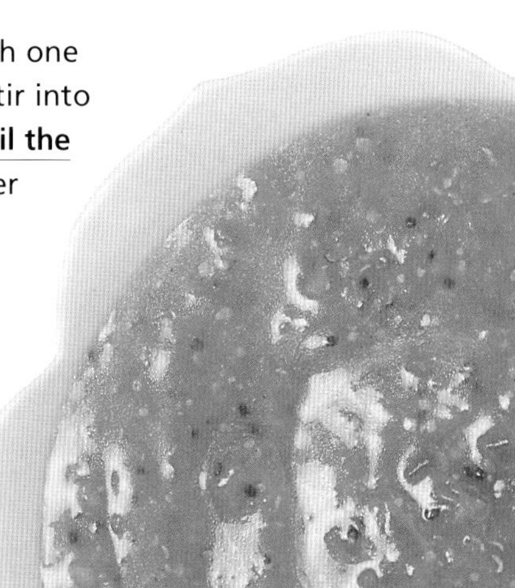

Corn Relish

Makes about 200ml (7fl oz)

YOU WILL NEED

1 small onion
1 celery stick
1 small red pepper
1 small carrot
100g (4oz) sweetcorn kernels, thawed if frozen
150ml (¼pt) vegetable stock
1 tablespoon lemon juice
salt and pepper
2 teaspoons cornflour

1

2

3

1 **Peel the onion** leaving the root on. Using the coarse side of the grater, grate the onion and place in a small saucepan. **Trim the celery** and wash well. Place on the chopping board and with a small sharp knife, **cut into very small dice**. Add to the saucepan.

2 **Cut the top off** the pepper and remove the seeds and pithy membrane. Rinse well and pat dry. Place on the chopping board and, with a small sharp knife, **cut into very small dice**. Add to the saucepan.

3 **Cut the top off the carrot and peel**. Again using the coarse side of the grater, **grate the carrot** then add to the saucepan.

4 Stir in the sweetcorn kernels, stock, lemon juice and seasoning to taste. Mix all the ingredients together.

5 Place the saucepan over a gentle heat and **bring to the boil**. Blend the cornflour to a smooth paste with one tablespoon of water and stir into the pan. **Cook, stirring until the mixture thickens** slightly. Cool before using. This relish will keep for up to one week, covered, in the refrigerator.

Measuring Charts

LIQUID MEASURES

Metric	Imperial
1.25 ml spoon	¼ teaspoon
2.5 ml spoon	½ teaspoon
5 ml spoon	1 teaspoon
15 ml spoon	1 tablespoon
25 ml	1 fl oz
50 ml	2 fl oz
65 ml	2½ fl oz
85 ml	3 fl oz
100 ml	3½ fl oz
120 ml	4 fl oz
135 ml	4½ fl oz
150 ml	¼ pint (5 fl oz) 8 tablespoons
175 ml	6 fl oz
200 ml	7 fl oz (⅓ pint)
250 ml	8 fl oz (1 US cup)
275 ml	9 fl oz
300 ml	½ pint (10 fl oz)
350 ml	12 fl oz
400 ml	14 fl oz
450 ml	¾ pint (15 fl oz)
475 ml	16 fl oz (2 US cups)
500 ml	18 fl oz
600 ml	1 pint (20 fl oz) 2½ US cups
750 ml	1¼ pints
900 ml	1½ pints
1 litre	1¾ pints
1.2 litres	2 pints
1.25 litres	2¼ pints
1.5 litres	2½ pints
1.6 litres	2¾ pints
1.7 litres	3 pints
2 litres	3½ pints
2.25 litres	4 pints
2.5 litres	4½ pints
2.75 litres	5 pints

SOLID MEASURES

Metric	Imperial	Metric	Imperial
10 g	¼ oz	400 g	14 oz
15 g	½ oz	425 g	15 oz
20 g	¾ oz	450 g	1 lb (16 oz)
25 g	1 oz	550 g	1¼ lb
40 g	1½ oz	675 g	1½ lb
50 g	2 oz	900 g	2 lb
65 g	2½ oz	1.25 kg	2½–2¾ lb
75 g	3 oz	1.5 kg	3–3½ lb
90 g	3½ oz	1.75 g	4–4½ lb
100 g	4 oz	2 kg	4½–4¾ lb
120 g	4½ oz	2.25 kg	5–5¼ lb
150 g	5 oz	2.5 kg	5½–5¾ lb
165 g	5½ oz	2.75 kg	6 lb
175 g	6 oz	3 kg	7 lb
185 g	6½ oz	3.5 kg	8 lb
200 g	7 oz	4 kg	9 lb
225 g	8 oz	4.5 kg	10 lb
250 g	9 oz	5 kg	11 lb
300 g	10 oz	5.5 kg	12 lb
325 g	11 oz	6 kg	13 lb
350 g	12 oz	6.5 kg	14 lb
375 g	13 oz	6.75 kg	15 lb

OVEN TEMPERATURES

Centigrade	Fahrenheit	Gas
110°	225°	¼
130°	250°	½
140°	275°	1
150°	300°	2
160°	325°	3
180°	350°	4
190°	375°	5
200°	400°	6
220°	425°	7
230°	450°	8